The Art of
Natural Family Planning®

Transitions
Student Guide

The Art of
Natural
Family
Planning®

Transitions
Student Guide

The Couple to Couple League
International, Inc.
P.O. Box 111184
Cincinnati, OH 45211-1184

This text is an integral part of The Couple to Couple League's (CCL) natural family planning instructional courses, specifically, the Postpartum and Premenopause Classes. Natural family planning is best learned through a live or online class series taught by a certified CCL teacher or through CCL's Home Study Program. For information on how to get in touch with a CCL certified teacher, visit the CCL website at **www.ccli.org**.

Book Design by Scott Bruno of b graphic design
Cover Photos by Ron Rack of Rack Photography

Cataloging data
        Library of Congress Control Number: 2013903555

The Art of Natural Family Planning® Transitions Student Guide:
Fertility Awareness for the Postpartum and Premenopause Transitions
The Couple to Couple League
Natural Family Planning
Birth Control
Breastfeeding
Sexual Morality
Postpartum
Premenopause

ISBN 978-0-926412-00-2

Published by The Couple to Couple League International, Inc.
P.O. Box 111184
Cincinnati, OH 45211
U.S.A.
800-745-8252
www.ccli.org

Printed in the United States
10 9 8 7 6 5 4 3 2 1

Table of Contents

Preface P

Couples who practice Natural Family Planning (NFP) will agree that when a woman's fertility is in a state of transition — such as following the birth of a baby or in the years

leading up to menopause — it can cause a degree of uncertainty and less confidence in their ability to effectively assess their fertility. Many couples contact The Couple to Couple League with questions during these times. We have seen their confidence grow when they better understand what is going on hormonally at these times and learn how to interpret their patterns of fertility and infertility.

This manual focuses on the practice of the Sympto-Thermal Method of NFP during these two major transition times — postpartum and premenopause — and accompanies CCL's classes dedicated solely to these times of transition.

Knowledge is empowering. It is our hope that this manual and CCL's Postpartum and Premenopause Classes will help NFP couples build greater confidence in their ability to effectively navigate the delicate times of transition.

Part I — Introduction & Review

Introduction • Review

Introduction 1

A woman's fertility is, by God's design, rhythmic or cyclic in nature. Over the years of practicing NFP, many couples come to enjoy this rhythm and appreciate anticipating the ebb and flow of the monthly hormonal symphony. This cyclic pattern changes or "transitions" during the time after childbirth and during premenopause.

Thus the purpose of this book is to assist couples in understanding these transitions and to continue to successfully practice NFP when they occur.

This book is divided into three major sections:
Part I — *Introduction & Review*; Part II — *Postpartum*; and Part III — *Premenopause*.

Part I — Introduction & Review has two lessons: *Introduction* and *Review*.

Summary: Part I — Introduction & Review

Lesson 1, *Introduction*, briefly explains the structure of the book and the various lessons it contains.

Lesson 2, *Review*, takes a look back at the basic hormones responsible for the fertility signs women observe during their normal reproductive cycles, the phases of the cycle, the fertility signs and their observations and the interpretation of an ovulatory cycle.

Part II — Postpartum is divided into six lessons: *The Postpartum Woman*; *Baby Feeding and Fertility*; *The Benefits of Breastfeeding*; *Fertility Awareness during Formula Feeding*; *Fertility Awareness during Breastfeeding*; and *NFP, Responsible Parenthood and Marital Intimacy*.

Summary: Part II — Postpartum Lessons

Lesson 3, *The Postpartum Woman*, explains how reproductive hormones function after childbirth in a way that can delay ovulation.

Lesson 4, *Baby Feeding and Fertility*, defines the various types of baby feeding and briefly discusses how each one can affect the return of fertility after childbirth.

Lesson 5, *The Benefits of Breastfeeding*, explains some of the many advantages of breastfeeding and how it provides the best nutrition for baby, assists mothers in recovering from childbirth and promotes a natural bond between mother and baby. In addition, breastfeeding can benefit the entire family, and it is recommended by both national and international organizations for a minimum of 12 months, and longer if possible.

Lesson 6, *Fertility Awareness during Formula Feeding*, explains how to record and interpret the signs of fertility after childbirth when a baby is fed formula. This lesson includes several charts for practice.

Lesson 7, *Fertility Awareness during Breastfeeding*, explains how to record and interpret the signs of fertility if a baby is breastfed. A variety of fertility patterns that can occur prior to the return of ovulatory cycles are explained. This lesson also includes several charts for practice.

Lesson 8, *NFP, Responsible Parenthood and Marital Intimacy*, initiates a discussion regarding the relationships between NFP, marital intimacy (which is broader than sexual intimacy) and responsible parenthood.

Part II — Postpartum **will help you to:**
- Recognize the hormonal changes during the postpartum transition
- Realize the benefits of breastfeeding
- Understand how baby feeding affects the return of fertility
- Identify the return of fertility and apply appropriate rules and guidelines whether you formula-feed or breastfeed your baby
- Discuss postpartum decisions regarding NFP, responsible parenthood and marital intimacy

Part III — Premenopause is divided into four lessons: *The Premenopause Woman, Fertility Awareness during Premenopause, What about Pregnancy?* and *Regarding Intimacy.*

Summary: Part III — Premenopause Lessons

Lesson 9, *The Premenopause Woman,* defines important terms regarding a woman's transition from premenopause to menopause, explains how the reproductive hormones function during this time and includes some reasons for these changes.

Lesson 10, *Fertility Awareness during Premenopause,* explains how to record and interpret the signs of fertility in the presence of different types of mucus patterns and other variations in the cycle. This lesson also includes several charts for practice.

Lesson 11, *What about Pregnancy?,* clarifies the possibility of achieving a pregnancy after age 40. It also contains important information for women who may be considering pregnancy during this stage of life.

Lesson 12, *Regarding Intimacy,* addresses the beauty of spousal intimacy during this time of life and offers a few suggestions for maintaining a healthy marital relationship.

Part III — Premenopause **will help you to:**

- Recognize hormonal changes during premenopause
- Understand how this transition affects fertility
- Apply appropriate rules and guidelines during premenopause
- Recognize potential changes to marital intimacy

Notes

2 Review

Lesson 2

This *Review* will ensure that you can properly identify the three phases of the menstrual cycle and know when and how to apply the Phase I Guidelines, Phase I Rules and the Sympto-Thermal Rule (ST Rule). This foundation in the Sympto-Thermal Method of NFP will help bring you confidence in reading and interpreting the signs of fertility during the transition times.

Phases of the Cycle

The female menstrual cycle can be divided into three phases. **Phase I** begins on the first day of menstrual bleeding and is a time of infertility.

Phase II begins at the onset of signs of fertility, and lasts a few days after the time of **ovulation** (when an egg is released from the ovary).

Phase III — is the post-ovulation time and is a time of infertility.

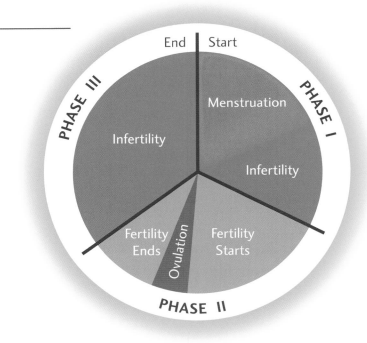

The three phases of the female cycle are the result of the interplay of four key hormones. Two hormones are produced by the pituitary gland — follicle stimulating hormone (FSH) and luteinizing hormone (LH). Two are produced within the female reproductive organs — estrogen and progesterone.

Review › Hormones

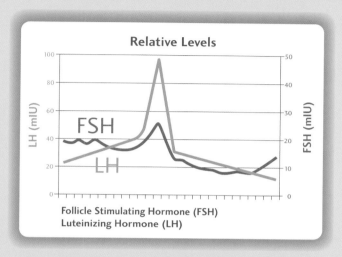

Relative Levels

FSH
LH

Follicle Stimulating Hormone (FSH)
Luteinizing Hormone (LH)

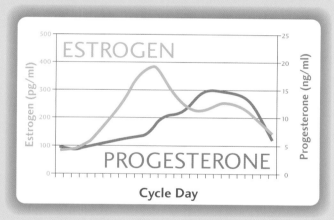

ESTROGEN

PROGESTERONE

Cycle Day

Female Hormones

Follicle stimulating hormone (FSH) is released by the pituitary gland during Phase I and stimulates the **follicles** (egg containers) within the ovaries to develop and mature. One of these follicles will become dominant. As the follicles grow and develop, they produce a second key hormone — estrogen.

Estrogen causes changes in a woman's body: mucus is produced indicating the beginning of Phase II, the cervix opens and softens and the lining of the uterus builds up. When a sufficient level of estrogen is reached, a message is sent to the pituitary gland to produce a surge in **luteinizing hormone (LH)**.

As luteinizing hormone travels from the pituitary gland to the ovary, it signals the release of the egg from the dominant follicle **(ovulation)**. The now empty follicle turns into a structure known as the **corpus luteum**. The corpus luteum takes on a very important function: in addition to continuing to produce estrogen, it also now produces progesterone.

Progesterone causes a number of notable effects on a woman's reproductive system. The cervix closes and hardens, the uterine lining continues to enrich, mucus thickens and dries up and basal body temperature rises. In addition, progesterone signals the pituitary gland to inhibit any further ovulations in that cycle.

Fertility Signs and their Observation

Cervical Mucus

Cervical mucus is an important fertility sign. The absence of mucus usually is a sign of infertility, and the presence of mucus usually indicates fertility. Mucus is an aid to fertility by providing both a swimming medium for sperm and nutrients that prolong sperm life. It also helps filter out abnormal sperm so that they do not reach the egg.

Mucus is identified throughout the day by detecting:

> 1) *Sensations*, what you can feel and sense; and
>
> 2) *Characteristics*, what you can see and touch

Begin mucus observations as soon as your period lessens (/ or •), or by Cycle Day 5, whichever occurs first. You can detect mucus sensations as you go about your normal activities throughout the day. These *sensations* occur outside the vagina at the labia, as a noticeable feeling of dryness, a feeling of being moist, sticky or damp, or as a feeling of wetness (similar to what occurs prior to the start of a menstrual period). Additionally, you can detect sensations of dryness or slipperiness when you wipe with toilet paper each time you use the bathroom.

You should record mucus sensations on the chart at the end of each day.

- Record "d" when you have an awareness of dryness throughout the day or when wiping.
- Record "m" when you have an awareness of moistness, stickiness, or dampness.
- Record "w" when you have an awareness of wetness.
- Record "sl" when you feel slippery when wiping.

Mucus characteristics can be identified visually and/or by checking their quality on the toilet paper after wiping during a bathroom visit. Like mucus sensations, you should begin checking for mucus characteristics as soon as your period lessens, or by Cycle Day 5, whichever comes first.

- Record "n" if there is no mucus observed.

- Record "t" if the mucus is tacky — sticky, thick, pasty, creamy, or clumpy.

- Record "s" if the mucus stretches repeatedly — very elastic, thin, stringy, or resembles raw egg white.

For mucus sensations and characteristics, be sure to record the *most fertile* observation of the day, even if later observations are not as fertile or dry, nothing.

Mucus Symbols

Symbols are used to document if the mucus observed on each cycle day was infertile (○), less fertile (⊖), or more fertile (⊕). The most fertile observation made each day in either sensations or characteristics determines the symbol used for that day.

SYMBOLS (mucus fertility)		CERVIX			
○	No mucus				
⊖	Less-fertile	h	Hard	•	Closed
⊕	More-fertile	so	Soft	○	Open

SENSATIONS		MUCUS SYMBOL	CHARACTERISTICS	
d	Dry	○	Nothing	n
m	Moist	⊖	Tacky	t
w,sl	Wet, slippery	⊕	Stretchy	s

Peak Day is the last day of the more fertile mucus before the drying-up process begins (i.e., the last day where a ⊕ symbol is recorded followed by ⊖ or ○ symbols). Peak day can only be identified in retrospect by comparing the two to three days after the last ⊕ to confirm it really is a drying-up process.

Temperature

Recall that **basal body temperature** is the temperature of the human body at rest or upon awakening, unaffected by food, drink or activity. During a typical fertility cycle, the basal body temperature is normally low before ovulation and then rises approximately 0.4° F after ovulation. The temperature remains high until the next menstruation, or if you are pregnant, throughout much of the pregnancy.

You should take your temperature at the same waking time each day. To maintain accuracy, it is best to remain in bed while taking it. Be sure to record the temperature on your chart daily.

Cervix

The cervix is an optional sign of fertility. Like mucus, the cervix changes in response to estrogen and progesterone. During Phase I of the cycle, the cervix is closed and hard. It opens and softens during Phase II, and returns to the closed and hard position during Phase III. The changes in the cervix coincide with the changes in mucus and temperature.

If you choose to observe the cervix, you should check it once or twice each day when visiting the bathroom, but only in the afternoon or evening. The cervix exam should not be done in the morning since the muscles that support the uterus contract during the night, making the cervix harder to reach. The muscles stretch somewhat after you have been up and around for a while.

You should record the cervix sign on the chart as "h" (hard) or "so" (soft) and "•" (closed) or "O" (open). A hard cervix feels like the tip of your nose while a soft cervix feels like your lower lip.

You can find all of the notations used for recording the mucus and cervix signs at the bottom left side of the chart.

Notes

Hormones & Fertility Signs

As discussed earlier, hormones cause the outward signs of fertility.

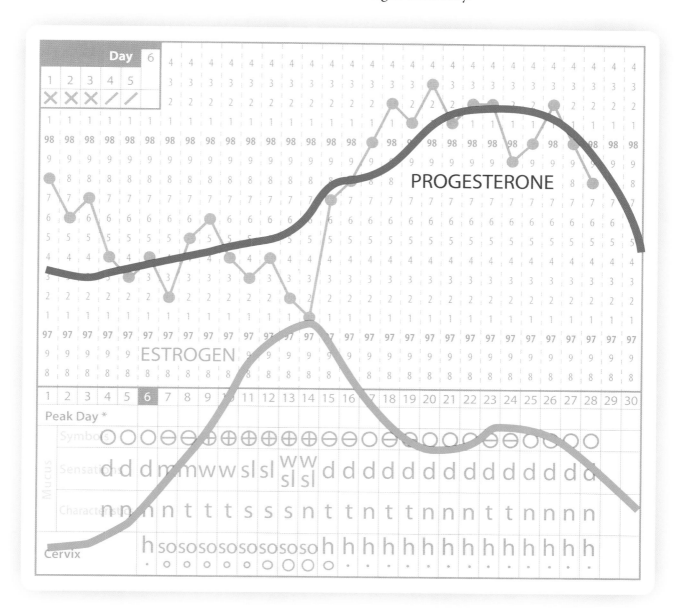

Declining progesterone from the previous cycle results in menstrual flow and the beginning of the next cycle. During the first few days of the cycle (Phase I) estrogen is low, then it begins to rise due to FSH stimulation of the follicles in the ovaries.

As the level of estrogen rises, the fertile time (Phase II) progresses; the mucus changes from less-fertile sensations and characteristics (moist, tacky) to more-fertile (wet, slippery, stretchy) up through ovulation. The cervix sign will follow a similar pattern, beginning to open and soften during Phase II. Over a period of days the opening/softening becomes more pronounced. Temperatures during Phases I and II remain low and may be more erratic in the early days of the cycle compared to mid-cycle.

A typical ovulatory mucus pattern is characterized by a few dry days as menstruation lessens, the appearance of less-fertile mucus days, followed by more-fertile mucus days that persist for a few days up through Peak Day. After Peak Day the mucus dries up.

After ovulation, the level of progesterone is higher than estrogen. With progesterone now the dominant hormone, the signs of fertility change again. Mucus begins to dry up, the cervix becomes harder and closes, and the temperature rises and remains high.

If pregnancy does not occur, both estrogen and progesterone levels drop at the end of the cycle. Thus, with the beginning of the next cycle (Phase I), menstruation returns, mucus is no longer produced, the cervix closes and hardens, and the temperature drops back to a lower level.

Patterns of mucus occurring without ovulation will be explained in detail in Lesson 7 for Postpartum and Lesson 10 for Premenopause.

Notes

Rules

A review of the Phase I and Phase III Rules will help ensure that you can properly apply them. This is the foundation of the Sympto-Thermal Method of NFP and will help bring you confidence in reading and interpreting your cycles.

Phase I Guidelines

When applying the rules to determine the limits of Phase I infertility, it is important to follow the two basic **Phase I Guidelines**. Once menstruation lessens (/ or •):

- **Evenings only:** Limit marital relations to evenings of dry, nothing mucus days during Phase I.

- **Not on consecutive days:** Abstain on any day that follows marital relations in Phase I unless you are experienced and can positively detect the absence of mucus.

Phase I Rules

Day 5/6 Rule

Assume infertility on Cycle Days 1–5.

For women with cycles 26 days or longer in the last 12 cycles, assume infertility on Cycle Days 1–6.

Conditions for use:
- This rule assumes the absence of mucus.

Doering Rule

Subtract seven from the earliest first day of temperature rise in the last 12 cycles. Mark that cycle day as the last day that you can assume Phase I infertility.

Conditions for use:
- This rule assumes the absence of mucus.
- This rule requires six cycles of temperature history.[1]

---

[1] While the last 12 cycles are considered when using the Doering Rule, only six are required to begin using it. Thus, with six cycles of temperature history, use six. With seven cycles of temperature history, use seven, and so on until you reach 12 cycles of history. From that point, continue to use the last 12 cycles of temperature history.

Last Dry Day Rule

The end of Phase I is the last day without mucus sensations or characteristics.

Conditions for use:

• This rule requires six cycles of experience.

• Women should have at least 6 days of mucus from its onset through Peak Day.

The Phase I rules have been summarized in this lesson. However, for a more detailed explanation, see *The Art of Natural Family Planning® Student Guide*, Class 2, Lesson 4, *The Transition from Phase I to Phase II*.

Phase III Rule

Sympto-Thermal Rule (ST Rule)

Phase III begins on the evening of:

1. The third day of drying-up after Peak Day, combined with

2. Three normal post-peak temperatures above the LTL, and

3. The third temperature at or above the HTL, or the cervix closed and hard for three days.

If the above conditions are not met, then Phase III begins after waiting an additional post-peak day for another temperature above the LTL.

(To review the steps for applying the ST Rule, see the Appendix, page 128)

Notes

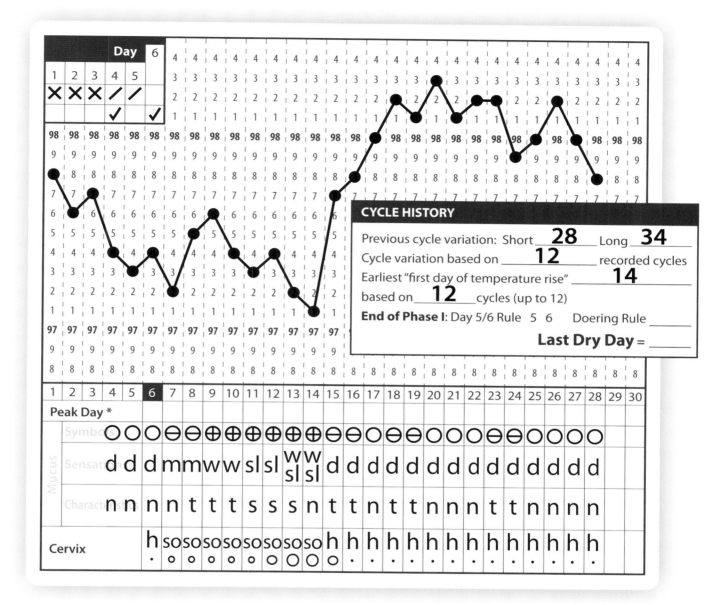

			Day	6																													

Day (row): 1 2 3 4 5 | 6 7 8 9 10 11 12 13 14 15 16 17 18 19 20 21 22 23 24 25 26 27 28 29 30

Row 1-5: ✗ ✗ ✗ ╱ ╱ with ✓ below 4, ✓ below 6

CYCLE HISTORY

Previous cycle variation: Short **28** Long **34**

Cycle variation based on **12** recorded cycles

Earliest "first day of temperature rise" **14**

based on **12** cycles (up to 12)

End of Phase I: Day 5/6 Rule 5 6   Doering Rule _____

Last Dry Day = _____

Peak Day *

	Symbol	Sensation	Character	Cervix

Symbol: ○ ○ ○ ⊖ ⊖ ⊕ ⊕ ⊕ ⊕ ⊖ ○ ⊖ ○ ○ ○ ⊖ ⊖ ○ ○ ○ ○

Mucus Sensation: d d d m m w w sl sl ww/sl ww/sl d d d d d d d d d d d d d

Character: n n n n t t t s s s n t t n t t n n n t t n n n

Cervix: h so so so so so so so so h h h h h h h h h h h h h h
· o o o o o o O O O o · · · · · · · · · · · ·

If you are attending the Postpartum or the Premenopause Class, you will complete this exercise in class. If you are using this Transitions Student Guide on your own, be sure to check your answers on page 129 of the Appendix.

1. Determine the end of Phase I by calculating:

   • Day 5/6 Rule (Circle the appropriate day on the chart and in the box.)

   • Doering Rule (Circle the appropriate day and record it in the box.)

   • Last Dry Day Rule

2. Draw a vertical line between Phase I and Phase II indicating the latest possible end of Phase I.

3. Determine the first day of Phase III by applying the ST Rule. Draw a vertical line through the temperature and circle that cycle day on the chart.

Be sure you understand how to properly analyze the review chart in this lesson before moving on. The lessons that follow assume that you understand Classes 1 and 2 of the main CCL course in Natural Family Planning. If you have any questions, contact a CCL Teaching Couple or the Central office for assistance.[2]

Notes

---

[2] NFP consulting is free for those who have received instruction from CCL (i.e.,Main Class Series or Home Study Course) and have a current CCL membership. Others may receive consulting help for a fee.

Part II — Postpartum

The Postpartum Woman • Baby Feeding and Fertility • The Benefits of Breastfeeding
Fertility Awareness during Formula Feeding • Fertility Awareness during Breastfeeding
NFP, Responsible Parenthood and Marital Intimacy

The Postpartum Woman $\quad$ 3

Lesson 3

Postpartum is the term used to explain that a mother has recently given birth and has not yet returned to her pre-pregnancy state. During this time, a mother will experience a variety of physical, psychological, physiological and perhaps even spiritual changes as she transitions from nurturing her baby in utero to nurturing him or her after birth.

Pregnancy and Postpartum Hormones

In the previous lesson you reviewed how the four key reproductive hormones — follicle stimulating hormone (FSH), luteinizing hormone (LH), estrogen and progesterone — interact during a woman's non-pregnant fertile years. During pregnancy, however, these hormones interact differently.

When pregnant, estrogen and progesterone rise considerably. They function in multiple ways to ensure that the pregnancy progresses smoothly, such as maintaining the **placenta** (the organ inside the uterus that supplies food and oxygen to, and removes wastes from, the unborn baby through the umbilical cord) and baby in the uterus, and further developing the mother's breasts for future milk production. In addition, **prolactin** (called "the mothering hormone") increases significantly and aids in the accelerated growth of breast tissue[3]

---

[3] Thomas W. Hilgers, M.D., *Reproductive Anatomy & Physiology*, 2nd edition (Omaha: Pope Paul VI Institute Press 2002), 46.

which is why the breasts contain fluid during the second half of pregnancy. After a woman delivers a baby and the placenta, estrogen and progesterone abruptly drop. The decrease in these two hormones helps stimulate the release of more prolactin from the pituitary gland, after which the level of prolactin becomes dependent on milk removal and breastfeeding.

Prolactin levels increase with suckling, and the hormone continues to stimulate and maintain the secretion of milk. Prolactin enables natural bonding between mother and baby that begins early in pregnancy, maximizes near delivery and then continues with the baby's suckling. The suckling also releases another hormone, **oxytocin**, which facilitates the let-down of milk during nursing and assists in this postpartum bonding.

As the pituitary gland increases its production of prolactin, it suppresses its production of LH. As long as LH remains low, ovulation is delayed, thus causing a time of natural infertility. This time of natural infertility varies greatly from woman to woman, depends on the type of baby feeding and is referred to as **lactational amenorrhea** (lack of menstrual periods due to breastfeeding, also known as breastfeeding amenorrhea). Breastfeeding, therefore, can greatly affect the length of lactational amenorrhea because it stimulates the production of prolactin and suppresses the hormones that are necessary for ovulation. On the other hand, when a woman feeds her baby formula and there is no suckling, there is usually a much shorter time before the first ovulation, as early as three weeks and typically within two to three months of birth.

Postpartum Hormones and Fertility Signs

While breastfeeding inhibits the hormones responsible for ovulation for a time, at some point suckling decreases as the baby gets older and ovulations will eventually return. Before that point, however, there may be months when the ovaries are stimulated but to a lesser degree. Ovarian stimulation means that estrogen is produced, but the degree to which estrogen is produced depends greatly on each woman's physiology and the baby's nursing routine.

> As the level of estrogen changes, it produces outward changing signs of fertility.

When the level of estrogen does change, women will notice some sort of change in the outward fertility signs, such as mucus or bleeding episodes not related to ovulation and menstruation. Mucus may appear because estrogen rises but then disappear as estrogen drops. Alternately, if the level of estrogen remains about the same, mucus could remain about the same for quite some time. All these variations are considered normal during this transition. Women who breastfeed will learn how to read and interpret these outward signs of fertility in Lesson 7.

Postpartum Hormones > Fertility Signs

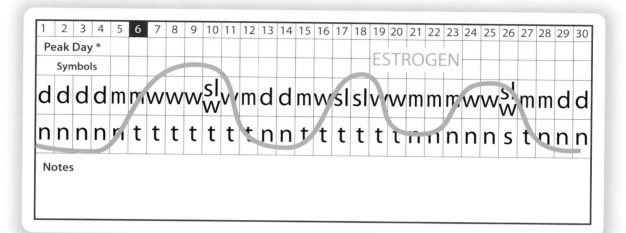

RELATIVE LEVEL OF ESTROGEN

TIME AFTER CHILDBIRTH

When estrogen is very low, mucus is not produced (dry, nothing days). As estrogen rises less-fertile mucus is produced (moist and/or tacky days), followed by more-fertile mucus (wet, slippery and/or stretchy days) when estrogen is even higher.

When there is no stimulation at the breast (i.e., formula feeding), the ovulation hormones are not suppressed resulting in an early return of fertility. Lesson 6 will explain how to read and interpret the signs of fertility when formula feeding.

4 Baby Feeding and Fertility

Lesson 4

In this lesson you will learn about the four types of baby feeding — formula feeding, mixed breastfeeding, exclusive breastfeeding and continued breastfeeding — and how each one can affect the return of fertility after childbirth.

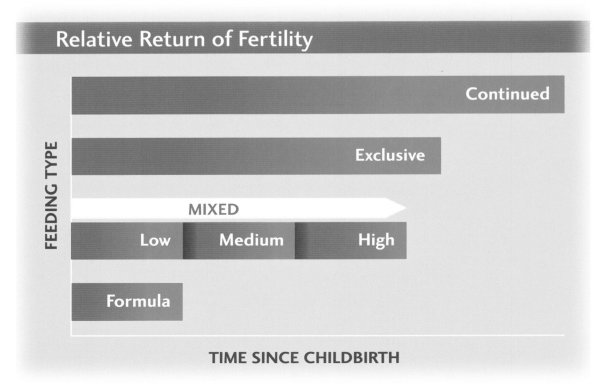

Formula Feeding

Formula feeding means that a baby is fed only formula with a bottle, ranging from cow's milk to specialty formulas. Typically, there is an early return of fertility postpartum, usually ranging from seven to nine weeks. (Note that while donated breast milk is not considered formula, couples who choose to feed their babies donated breast milk should apply the fertility awareness instructions associated with formula feeding explained in Lesson 6 — Fertility Awareness during Formula Feeding.)

Breastfeeding

Over the years family planning and lactation experts have studied the return of fertility in women who breastfeed. They have observed that the return to fertility or the length of lactational amenorrhea varies greatly. Further research led to the identification of several key factors that influence the length of breastfeeding amenorrhea. These factors include:

> Mother's physiology also influences when fertility returns.

- **Duration** of breastfeeding (the number of months)
- **Frequency** of breastfeeding (the number of feedings within 24 hours)
- **Intensity** of breastfeeding (influenced by how long the baby nurses at each feeding, the use of bottles, pacifiers, solid foods and other factors)
- **Mother's physiology** (individual physiology is unique and varies from woman to woman)

The return of fertility is quite variable and very individual. In a few cases, breastfeeding women may begin ovulating a few months after giving birth. In other cases, breastfeeding women may not get their fertility back until after weaning. This wide spectrum of the return of fertility is particularly common in mixed breastfeeding.

Notes

Mixed breastfeeding (or formula feeding) is a combination of breastfeeding and supplementing with formula and/or pumped breast milk. It may also include an early introduction of solids, regular pacifier use, limiting the amount of time that the baby suckles and/or scheduled nursing. (Mixed breastfeeding also includes those times when a baby is fed exclusively with his mother's pumped milk.)

Lactation experts use the following terminology to differentiate between different types of mixed breastfeeding because it may provide some frame of reference for anticipating the return of fertility:

- High mixed breastfeeding — 80% of the feeding is at the breast
- Medium mixed breastfeeding — 20–79% of the feeding is at the breast
- Low mixed breastfeeding — Less than 20% of the feeding is at the breast

Thus mixed breastfeeding does delay ovulation, but the return of fertility varies greatly, depending on the amount of suckling and the mother's physiology.

Exclusive breastfeeding is defined as nursing whenever the baby indicates a desire (day or night) during his first six months of life.[4] The baby derives all of his nutrition from the breast, and he receives no bottles or early solids. The baby stays near his mother so that he can nurse and pacify at the breast on his own schedule; he does not regularly use a pacifier.

Research shows that, generally, mothers who exclusively breastfeed are highly infertile during this time. Much of this evidence was gathered at a conference held in Bellagio, Italy in 1988.[5] Family planning experts from around the world tracked the return of fertility in mothers who were not using any method of family planning or fertility awareness while they were exclusively breastfeeding. Their findings revealed significant infertility in the first 56 days (eight

---

[4] After six months postpartum, the baby receives other nourishment in addition to breast milk, and the mother is in the category of *continued breastfeeding*.

[5] K. Kennedy, R. Rivera, and A. McNeilly, "Consensus statement on the use of breastfeeding as a family planning method," *Contraception* 39:5 (May 1989) 477–496. From the Bellagio Consensus Conference on Lactational Infertility, Bellagio, Italy, August 1988.

weeks) postpartum, and less than a two percent chance of becoming pregnant with no bleeding episodes occurring after 8 weeks during the first six months postpartum.[6,7] This high rate of infertility (approximately 98%) has been observed repeatedly in subsequent studies.[8,9,10,11] In fact, the evidence is so solid that it is classified as its own method of family planning (with its own set of guidelines) and is called the **Lactational Amenorrhea Method (LAM).**[12]

Continued breastfeeding means nursing beyond six months, when other foods and liquids are added to complement the breast milk. The baby still nurses and pacifies at the breast on his own schedule. The increased duration of breastfeeding brings significant health and development benefits to the child and the mother. It can lead to extended infertility, beyond one year. Over time, a baby nurses less for nutrition and more for comfort. The American Academy of Pediatrics (AAP), an important organization of doctors who care for infants and young children, strongly encourages continued breastfeeding: "There is no upper limit to the duration of breastfeeding and no evidence of psychologic or developmental harm from breastfeeding into the third year of life or longer."[13]

Notes

[6] *The Consensus Statement* used the terms "Fully or nearly fully breastfeeding" and it was defined as exclusive breastfeeding or nearly exclusive with slight supplementation, from a few swallows up to less than one feeding per day. The Couple to Couple League uses the term "exclusive breastfeeding" because it is a commonly used medical term; however, CCL's definition is stronger as it allows no supplementation.

[7] A. Perez, M. Labbok, and J. Queenan, "A Clinical Study of the Lactational Amenorrhea Method for Family Planning," *Lancet* 339 (1992) 968–970.

[8] K. Kennedy, M. Labbok, and P. Van Look, "Consensus Statement: Lactational Amenorrhea Method for Family Planning," *Int J Gynaecol Obstet* 54 (1996) 55–57.

[9] World Health Organization Task Force on Methods for the Natural Regulation of Fertility, "The World Health Organization multinational study of breast-feeding and lactational amenorrhea. IV. Postpartum bleeding and lochia in breast-feeding women," *Fertil Steril* 72:3 (1999) 441–447.

[10] Ibid., 431–440.

[11] M. Labbok, V. Hight-Laukaran, Anne Peterson, Veronica Fletcher, Helena von Hertzen, Paul Van Look, et al., "Multicenter Study of the Lactational Amenorrhea Method (LAM) I. Efficacy, Duration, and Implications for Clinical Application," *Contraception* 55 (May/June 1997) 327–336.

[12] The Couple to Couple League does not promote exclusive breastfeeding as a method of family planning, and does not specifically promote LAM; this information is included because it has been well researched. While appreciating the infertility breastfeeding can bring, CCL promotes fertility awareness and making decisions based upon reading and interpreting fertility signs.

[13] "2005 AAP Policy Statement of Breastfeeding and the Use of Human Milk," *Pediatrics*, Vol. 115, No. 2 (February 2005) 500.

5 The Benefits of Breastfeeding

Lesson 5

Human mothers (as well as other mammals) are uniquely designed to produce milk for their offspring. For thousands of years human mothers have breastfed their infants,

instinctively knowing it was best for their babies. After formulas were developed and made accessible to the general public, there was a conspicuous decline in breastfeeding in the mid-1900s. In the 1950s, however, pro-breastfeeding mothers decided to renew interest in breastfeeding because of its many benefits. Eventually, they formalized a group which is now known as La Leche League International (LLLI) (*www.llli.com*). For over 60 years La Leche League has been the primary source of support and information for women who wish to breastfeed in a culture where formula feeding has become prevalent.

Today there is a much stronger emphasis placed on breastfeeding, and within the medical community as well. Now, more than ever, massive scientific evidence exists to support breastfeeding. The AAP considers breastfeeding to be so important that it provides an extensive set of instructions for pediatricians and other health care professionals to protect, promote and support breastfeeding, "…not only in their individual practices but also in the hospital, medical school, community and nation."[14] The AAP even goes so far as to challenge these experts to provide advice to adoptive mothers who decide to breastfeed through **induced lactation** (the process by which a non-pregnant mother is stimulated to **lactate** — produce milk).

Benefits of Breastfeeding › Baby

Nutritional

Breastfeeding provides the best nutrition for babies. Breast milk cannot be duplicated due to its living properties and ever-changing composition; in other words, it conforms perfectly to the needs of the baby at each stage of development, even if the baby is born prematurely. It is easy to digest and readily available. For the first six months, this single food source offers optimum nutrition for the baby.

Immunological

Following delivery, a yellowish liquid called **colostrum** is secreted by a mother's breasts for about the first three to five days. This powerful substance is a different composition from the breast milk produced later. Colostrum is rich in **antibodies** (proteins that fight infections), contains more protein and minerals than breast milk, and less sugar and fat, which is just what a baby needs immediately after birth. As breast milk is produced, it is *species specific* and *mother and baby specific*. Such specificity provides a baby with the best chance of survival.

Breastfeeding enhances a child's overall health. In the United States, post-neonatal infant mortality rates are reduced by 21% in breastfed babies.[15] In addition, breast milk provides protection against viral, bacterial and allergic diseases.[16]

Breastfeeding also acts as an analgesic during a painful procedure (such as a heel stick on a newborn), and cognitive development studies show better performance in breastfed babies compared with formula-fed infants.[17] Furthermore, the AAP cites studies that suggest "decreased rates of sudden infant death syndrome (SIDS) in the first year of life and reduction in incidence of insulin-dependent (type 1) and non-insulin-dependent (type 2) diabetes mellitus, lymphoma, leukemia and Hodgkin's disease, overweight and obesity, hypercholesterolemia and asthma in older children and adults who were breastfed, compared with individuals who were not breastfed."[18]

---

[14] 2005 AAP Policy Statement, 496.

[15] 2005 AAP Policy Statement, 496.

[16] Jon Weimer, *The Economic Benefits of Breastfeeding* (Economic Research Service/USDA, 2001) 10.

[17] 2005 AAP Policy Statement, 497.

[18] 2005 AAP Policy Statement, 496–497.

Psychological

Babies have a basic need to be close to their mothers. Mothers are their protectors as well as their source of nourishment. Closeness, therefore, reduces stress for them. This early dependence and trust leads to independence later because the child knows he can always return to mother for help and protection. Breastfeeding enables babies to experience the maternal heartbeat, a familiar intrauterine sound. Breastfed infants are more advanced developmentally, more outgoing and assertive and socialize better.

Cognitive

Breastfed babies have better neurological development and more rapid development of visual function and motor skills, and these cognitive benefits increase with continued breastfeeding. One study in the May 2008 *Archives of General Psychiatry* found that children who were exclusively breastfed scored, on average, 7.5 points higher in verbal intelligence, 2.9 points higher in nonverbal intelligence and 5.9 points higher in overall intelligence. These results were found to be directly proportional to the amount of breast milk ingested in relation to the weight of the baby. Others suggest the cognitive edge is due in part to the improved mother-infant interaction during breastfeeding.

Benefits of Breastfeeding › Mother

Breastfeeding not only benefits babies, it also benefits mothers in multiple ways. For example, it promotes natural bonding between mother and baby through the combined action of the hormones prolactin and oxytocin (discussed earlier). Oxytocin produces a calming effect and helps decrease a mother's anxiety and increase her attention to her baby. Recall that oxytocin, released during breastfeeding, is responsible for producing the let-down reflex that makes breast milk available to the baby. This same hormone also causes the uterine muscles to contract, which decreases postpartum bleeding and enables the uterus to return to its pre-pregnancy size. Because oxytocin is so beneficial for decreasing postpartum blood loss, most doctors and midwives encourage mothers to breastfeed their newborns immediately after giving birth. Newborns are usually most alert and ready to suckle at this time.

There are several other advantages for mothers who nurse their babies. Most mothers who breastfeed will enjoy some time of postpartum infertility. This time of natural infertility is an opportunity for a mother to recover from the pregnancy and delivery. Many women appreciate that it also helps them return to their pre-pregnancy weight sooner. It has also been known to decrease the risks of breast and ovarian cancers, and possibly even to decrease the risk of hip fractures and osteoporosis in postmenopausal women who breastfed their babies.[19]

---

[19] 2005 AAP Policy Statement, 497.

Benefits of Breastfeeding › Family

Breastfeeding can cause a positive chain reaction within a family: The infant receives sound nutrition and comfort when he nurses; the mother acquires short term and long term health benefits; and more time can be devoted to other family members because of decreased infant illness and the fact that the baby's food is always ready — no preparation time needs to be factored into the family's schedule.

In addition, a family in the United States saves an average of $900–$1,200 yearly[20] that would otherwise be spent on formula. Furthermore, in its discussion of the benefits of breastfeeding, the AAP includes "the potential for decreased annual health care costs of $3.6 *billion* [emphasis added] in the United States…and decreased parental employee absenteeism and associated loss of income…"[21]

Breastfeeding Advocates

Other eminent organizations have joined the AAP in advocating exclusive breastfeeding[22] for the first six months of an infant's life. Among these organizations are the American College of Obstetricians and Gynecologists (ACOG), the American Academy of Family Physicians, the Academy of Breastfeeding Medicine (ABM), the World Health Organization (WHO), the United Nation's Children's Fund and several other health organizations.[23] Furthermore, the AAP recommends continued breastfeeding as the standard of care for all babies for a minimum of 12 months, and the WHO recommends breastfeeding for a minimum of 24 months.[24] The Couple to Couple League also advocates exclusive breastfeeding and promotes continued breastfeeding with baby-led weaning.

To learn more about the value of breastfeeding, you can read *The Art of Breastfeeding* by Linda Kracht and Jackie Hilgert (Cincinnati: The Couple to Couple League, 2008).

---

[20] J. Lauwers and A. Swisher, *Counseling the Nursing Mother, A Lactation Consultant's Guide*, 2005, 177.

[21] 2005 AAP Policy Statement, 497.

[22] 2005 AAP Policy Statement, 498. "Exclusive breastfeeding is defined as an infant's consumption of human milk with no supplementation of any type (no water, no juice, no nonhuman milk, and no foods) except for vitamins, minerals, and medications."

[23] Ibid.

[24] Lauwers and Swisher, 167; *Pediatrics*, Vol. 115, No. 2, February 2005, 496–506; World Health Organization, *Infant and young child nutrition: Global strategy on infant and young child feeding*, Fifty-fifth World Health Assembly, 16 April 2002.

6 Fertility Awareness during Formula Feeding

Lesson 6

Most new birth mothers who feed their babies formula will experience at least a few weeks of postpartum amenorrhea, but overall their fertility returns quickly. Ovulatory cycles usually return between two and three months after childbirth. If formula feeding, you may initially experience one (or more) bleedings not preceded by a thermal shift and many days of mucus. Soon, however, ovulation followed by menstruation will occur. The first few cycles will be longer than normal due to extended Phase II's and shorter luteal phases, but cycles will return to their pre-pregnancy lengths in a few short months.

This early return of fertility is because lactating hormones that inhibit ovulation are not being produced. Studies show that by the end of the third month postpartum, 91% of non-lactating mothers have had at least one period,[25] an indication that fertility is returning.

In order to identify the return to fertility, couples need to know when to begin observing and charting the three key fertility signs — mucus, temperature, cervix. Before discussing these in detail, it is important to be able to detect the difference between **lochia**, an after-childbirth discharge, and cervical mucus. Mucus signals the start of fertility, or Phase II, and could appear rather early.

---

[25] Ruth Lawrence and Robert Lawrence, *Breastfeeding: A Guide for the Medical Professional* (Elsevier Mosby, 2005) 738.

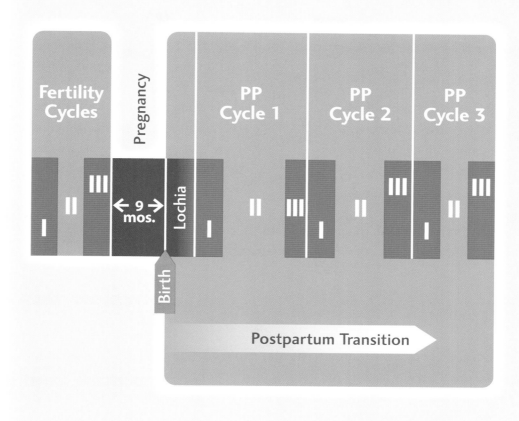

Lochia

For about three to six weeks postpartum, women produce a blood-tinged discharge called lochia. Lochia occurs because the uterus is contracting and shrinking back to its pre-pregnancy size, and the endometrium is regenerating after the nine months of pregnancy. For the first few days after childbirth, the lochia is generally dark red to brownish. Once blood flow decreases, it becomes thinner and brownish. At approximately two weeks postpartum, lochia becomes thick and white to yellowish in appearance. This is all part of the normal healing process and regeneration of the uterine lining, so that a baby might potentially implant at the same site in the future. The white or yellow discharge may look somewhat similar to cervical mucus, but it is not related to fertility. It continues for about three to six weeks postpartum, gradually decreasing in amount until it is gone.

For more information on lochia, see page 150–151 in the Reference Guide.

The three key fertility signs:

1. Mucus

Because of the early return of fertility when formula feeding, begin observing and recording mucus **as soon as the lochia lessens**. If you are experienced with observing mucus and do not detect any, you can assume Phase I infertility. Resume marital relations when cleared by your doctor, and be sure to follow the Phase I Guidelines. Note that by the time you are cleared to resume marital relations, you may already be observing mucus.

> Begin mucus observations as soon as lochia lessens. Remember, mucus observations are external only.

If you are inexperienced with mucus observations, contact your Teaching Couple or the CCL Central office for guidance, or consider abstaining if you have a serious need to avoid a pregnancy.

Phase I Guidelines

Evenings only: Remember that an infertile day is only determined after checking for mucus throughout the day; therefore, marital relations should be reserved for the evening. You may not notice any mucus during the day, but then detect some mucus in the evening. If this occurs, consider yourself in Phase II because you detected mucus.

Not on consecutive days: Marital relations leave seminal residue in the vaginal area. If you detect this residue during your mucus checks the following day, the seminal residue could mask the presence of mucus. You cannot assume you are infertile unless you are sure that there is no mucus present. Therefore, you should abstain on any day that follows marital relations in Phase I unless you are experienced and can positively differentiate between seminal residue and mucus.

Phase II

Assume Phase II when mucus sensations or characteristics are detected. Since **non-menstrual bleeding** (spotting/bleeding not preceded by a thermal shift) can also occur, this is also considered Phase II. However, more than likely, you will observe the onset of mucus as your first indicator of the start of Phase II.

When formula feeding, once mucus or bleeding occurs a couple should consider themselves in Phase II until a thermal shift occurs and the ST Rule can be applied. Even if mucus disappears for a time, consider yourselves in Phase II until you have a sympto-thermal interpretation for Phase III.

Reminders

- When formula feeding, Phase II begins when mucus or bleeding occurs, and continues until the ST Rule can be applied for Phase III.

- Abstinence could be lengthy if you are trying to postpone pregnancy.

- Show your love in non-genital ways; be patient with one another.

The three key fertility signs:

2. Temperature

In addition to observing your mucus signs, begin taking your temperatures **as soon as lochia lessens**.

Be sure to record temperature signs on the chart, along with your mucus observations, and apply the Sympto-Thermal Rule when able.

The three key fertility signs:

3. Cervix

As you may recall from previous classes, the cervix observation is optional with regard to the Sympto-Thermal Method of NFP. After childbirth, it is important to note that the cervix needs time to heal and should not be examined until your doctor gives permission to resume sexual intercourse with your husband.

If you are familiar with the cervix observation and this is your first baby, you may notice that the cervix seems more open than it did previously. Prior to having a baby, typically the opening to the cervix is more round. After childbirth, you may notice changes, such as the opening may be more like a horizontal slit, or it may even be a bit curved at the ends of the slit. However it feels, realize that this may constitute a new normal standard for you when comparing how the cervix changes.

Note that when checking the cervix, you may occasionally detect mucus at the cervical os, or opening of the cervix. Mucus can change in its characteristics as it migrates from the os to the labia; in some cases, it never reaches the external labia. Furthermore, the clinical studies evaluating effectiveness have only examined external mucus observations. Therefore, only mucus found externally should be considered a sign of fertility. Any mucus found at the cervical os when checking the cervix should be ignored.

• Do not record any mucus observed at the cervical os.

For beginners, it is best to start the cervix check during Phase III because it is easier to locate the cervix at this time, and it will provide you with a guideline with which to compare the cervix checks you do in future cycles. Follow the instructions explained in Lesson 2 — *Review*, or *The Art of Natural Family Planning® Student Guide*, Lesson 3.

Summary of Fertility Awareness when Formula Feeding

Everything that you have just learned with regard to applying fertility awareness while formula feeding can be summarized as follows:

- As soon as the lochia lessens, start observing and recording mucus and temperature

  - If you have no mucus, assume Phase I infertility and apply the Phase I Guidelines

  - When mucus and/or bleeding return, assume Phase II fertility

- Make the optional cervix exam when you can resume marital relations as per your doctor's instructions

- Apply the ST Rule when possible

A flow diagram capturing this Summary of Fertility Awareness during Formula Feeding is located on page 151 of the Reference section.

Postpartum Charting Hints

Number your charts

When you are postpartum and not experiencing normal, monthly ovulatory cycles, you may find the following numbering technique useful. If charting for the first time (i.e., you are new to practicing NFP), label your first chart as 1a. Subsequent charts can be labeled as 1b, 1c, etc. until you ovulate. The chart following the first ovulation would be labeled as Chart 2. This technique is especially helpful when your teacher or consultant reviews your charts. If you have charted your fertility signs prior to this, follow the number from your last chart when you conceived. For example, if it was 15, then number your postpartum charts as 16a, 16b, 16c and so forth until you ovulate. The chart following your first ovulation would then be labeled 17.

Make notes on your chart

Continue using the Notes section of your chart to record significant events such as:

- the age or birth date of your baby
- how you are feeding him
- your six-week postpartum checkup
- when lochia lessens

Continue charting on same chart

Remember that as your fertility returns you will likely experience non-menstrual bleeds before your first ovulation. Therefore, do not start a new chart with the appearance of bleeding unless it has been preceded by a Peak Day, mucus dry-up and thermal shift; if not, continue charting on the same chart.

Notes

Formula Feeding > Practice Chart 1

The practice charts that follow illustrate how to interpret your fertility signs if you are feeding your baby formula.

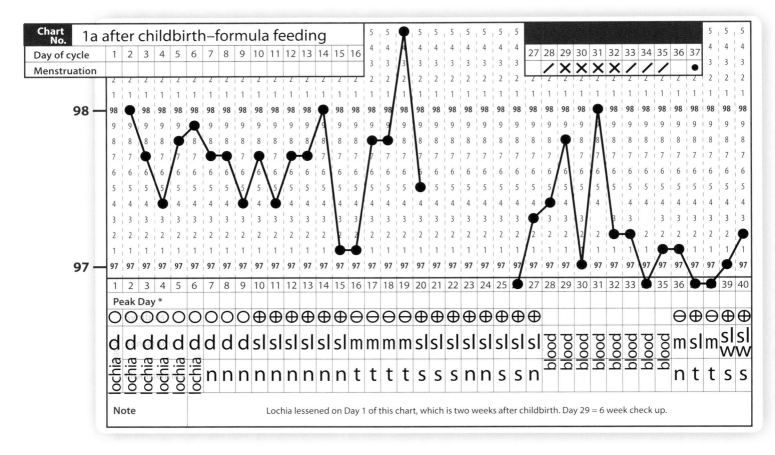

If you are attending the Postpartum Class, you will complete this exercise in class. If you are using this Transitions Student Guide on your own, be sure to check your answers on page 130 of the Appendix.

1. Draw a vertical line between the last day of Phase I and the first day of Phase II.

2. Mark Peak Day and number the dry-up days that follow (i.e., P 1 2 3).

3. Determine the pre-shift six temperatures.

4. Set the LTL and HTL.

5. Apply the ST Rule to determine the beginning of Phase III infertility. Draw a vertical line through the temperature and circle that cycle day on the chart.

Formula Feeding > Practice Chart 2

This chart is a continuation from Practice Chart 1.

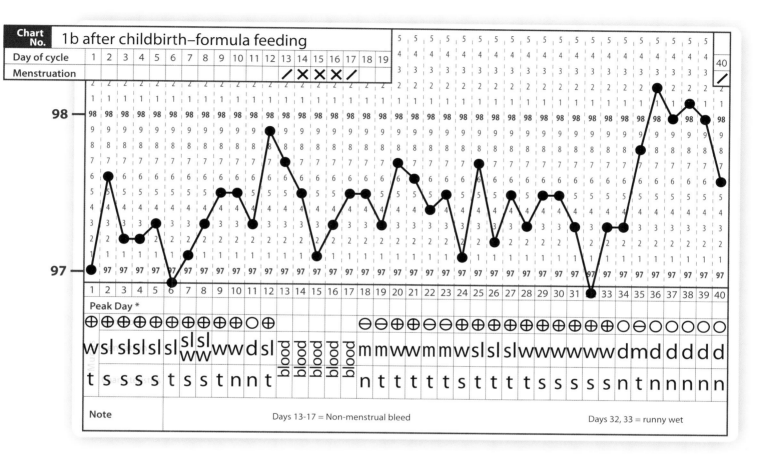

If you are attending the Postpartum Class, you will complete this exercise in class. If you are using this Transitions Student Guide on your own, be sure to check your answers on page 131 of the Appendix.

1. Draw a vertical line between the last day of Phase I and the first day of Phase II.

2. Mark Peak Day and number the dry-up days that follow (i.e., P 1 2 3).

3. Determine the pre-shift six temperatures.

4. Set the LTL and HTL.

5. Apply the ST Rule to determine the beginning of Phase III infertility. Draw a vertical line through the temperature and circle that cycle day on the chart.

Note that in this long, single cycle there were very few days without mucus (d,n) prior to ovulation and many days with mucus. When formula feeding, estrogen is not being suppressed, which can result in nearly continuous mucus. Consider all days from the first onset of mucus (or bleeding) to be fertile and in Phase II until you can interpret for the start of Phase III.

These two charts (Charts 1a and 1b) also illustrate a Phase II that is much longer than usual. It is interrupted twice with non-menstrual bleeding episodes. Ovulation finally occurs late on Chart 1b. It is normal to have a short luteal phase with the first ovulation (in this case, five days). A long cycle, long Phase II and short luteal phase are typical occurrences for the first few cycles after childbirth.

Over the course of a few cycles, you will notice that your cycle lengths and Phase IIs will gradually shorten, while the luteal phases will gradually lengthen to your pre-pregnancy lengths. After you start ovulating, you may apply the Phase I rules on subsequent cycles; however, do not consider cycle lengths during this transition time in their application. Use your pre-pregnancy cycle history data to calculate Phase I until your postpartum cycles have returned to normal lengths.

Notes

Fertility Awareness during Breastfeeding

Lesson 7

As you learned in Lesson 4, mothers who breastfeed generally have a later return of fertility, dependent upon the type of breastfeeding. The delay is usually longer with exclusive breastfeeding than with mixed breastfeeding, but not in all cases. Some mothers who exclusively breastfeed may still experience an earlier return of fertility, while some mothers who practice mixed breastfeeding may experience a delay in the return of fertility. As mentioned previously, this varies based on the duration, frequency, and intensity of the feedings, as well as each woman's own unique physiology.

> Observing and recording the signs of fertility will identify if ovulation occurs prior to the first bleeding episode.

Many women will notice an absence of fertility signs or a pattern of mucus that is infertile. When the signs of fertility do begin to appear, instead of immediately returning to ovulatory cycles that pass through Phases I, II, and III, you may shift back and forth between Phase I and Phase II for a while — often several months — before experiencing the first postpartum ovulation. Frequently breastfeeding mothers will ovulate prior to their first bleeding episode, but this is not problematic when diligently observing and recording the signs of fertility.

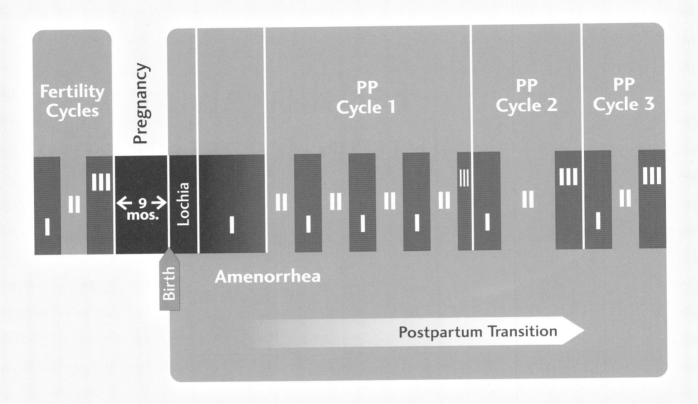

If you have given birth to other children and you are feeding your baby the same way, your past experience may provide general guidance on what to expect with this child. But it is the absence or presence of the signs of fertility that ultimately determines whether or not your fertility is returning.

In order to identify the return to fertility, couples need to know when to begin observing and charting the three key fertility signs: mucus, temperature and cervix. Before discussing these in detail, it is important to be able to detect the difference between **lochia**, an after-childbirth discharge, and cervical mucus. Mucus signals the start of fertility, or Phase II.

Lochia

For about three to six weeks postpartum, women produce a blood-tinged discharge called lochia. Lochia occurs because the uterus is contracting and shrinking back to its pre-pregnancy size, and the endometrium is regenerating after the nine months of pregnancy. For the first few days after childbirth, the lochia is generally dark red to brownish. Once blood flow decreases, it becomes thinner and brownish. At approximately two weeks postpartum, lochia becomes thick and white to yellowish in appearance. This is all part of the normal healing process and regeneration of the uterine lining, so that a baby might potentially implant at the same site in the future. The white or yellow discharge may look somewhat similar to cervical mucus, but it is not related to fertility. It continues for about three to six weeks postpartum, gradually decreasing in amount until it is gone.

For more information on lochia, see page 150–151 in the Reference Guide.

The three key measurable signs of fertility:

1. Mucus

For women who breastfeed, mucus observations should begin as soon as the lochia lessens. When mucus or bleeding is detected, begin taking temperatures and recording both mucus and temperature on the chart.

> Begin mucus observations as soon as lochia lessens. Start charting mucus and temperatures as soon as mucus and/or bleeding first occurs.

If you are experienced with making mucus observations, you can assume Phase I infertility if you do not observe any mucus. Do not resume marital relations until you are cleared by your doctor. Follow the Phase I Guidelines explained on the next page. If you are inexperienced, ask your Teaching Couple how to proceed. If you are learning this on your own, consider the following guidance:

Becoming confident at making and assessing your mucus observation requires daily observations over a period of time. After a few days of observing for the presence or absence of mucus, most women can easily tell that they feel dry and do not see any mucus. If you are confident that there is no mucus present, follow the Phase I Guidelines. If you are not confident with the mucus sign, consider contacting a Teaching Couple or the CCL Central office for further advice.

Reminder

- Husbands can be especially helpful during this time by encouraging their wives to get into (or back into) the routine of observing their fertility signs daily, and by recording this information for their wives on the chart when it is appropriate.

Phase I Guidelines

Evenings only: Remember that an infertile day is only determined after checking for mucus throughout the day, therefore, marital relations should be reserved for the evening. You may not notice any mucus during the day, but then detect some mucus in the evening. If this occurs, consider yourself in Phase II because you detected mucus.

Not on consecutive days: Marital relations leave seminal residue in the vaginal area. If you detect this residue during your mucus checks the following day, the seminal residue could mask the presence of mucus. You cannot assume you are infertile unless you are sure that there is no mucus present. Therefore, you should abstain on any day that follows marital relations in Phase I unless you are experienced and can positively differentiate between seminal residue and mucus.

Phase II

Assume Phase II when mucus sensations or characteristics are detected. Since spotting/bleeding not preceded by a thermal shift (**non-menstrual bleeding**) can also occur, this too is considered Phase II. In some cases, a non-menstrual bleed will be your first indication that you have begun Phase II; you may not notice any mucus before the bleeding episode begins. Once mucus or bleeding occurs Phase II begins. However, when breastfeeding, mucus often subsides and Phase I returns. In time, mucus will return and along with it Phase II. This shifting back and forth between Phases I and II may occur for many months because of the effects of breastfeeding. How to interpret this "dance" between the fertile and infertile times is the subject of the rest of this lesson.

Mucus may vary during breastfeeding. It could be:

- Absent
- Present in different patterns
  - Patches
  - With non-menstrual spotting/bleeding
  - Continuous
    - Unchanging
    - Changing

When Mucus is Absent

Previously we reviewed that the absence of both mucus sensations and mucus characteristics indicates infertility. Thus, if you have no mucus after the lochia lessens, consider yourself in Phase I infertility.

When Mucus is Present in Different Patterns

The key to understanding why different patterns of mucus occur during the postpartum transition is to recognize that they are directed by hormones. In Lesson 2 we reviewed how estrogen builds throughout the fertile time, causing mucus to change from less-fertile to more-fertile. During the postpartum time, mucus still follows the level of estrogen, but is manifested differently because ovulation may not be imminent. When the level of estrogen rises and then falls, mucus will appear and then disappear. If estrogen rises but then remains the same, mucus will appear and also stay about the same. Estrogen may rise sporadically causing a few random days of more-fertile mucus, but it does not continually rise. Thus, as estrogen rises and falls, mucus changes accordingly.

> When estrogen rises and falls, mucus patterns follow.

To Identify Different Patterns of Mucus

To best assess how mucus changes during the postpartum time, you will need more detail than the broad descriptions (i.e., tacky, stretchy) and letters you use during regular fertility cycles. Therefore, you should write brief descriptions of your mucus sensations and characteristics. Be specific and avoid general terms like tacky or stretchy. Use any words that you think best describe what you are observing.

At the end of each day's observations, compare today's observation with that of the previous day. If the mucus is about the same, use the same word(s) to describe it; if it differs, use a different word(s) to describe it and record on the chart.

Assume Phase II fertility during this time.

Examples of brief descriptions

Sensations

slightly moist, moist

slightly damp, damp

slightly sticky, sticky

drippy, swampy

slightly slippery, slippery

very slippery, wet, watery, runny

Characteristics

sticky, big thick glob

small clumps

pasty, creamy, milky

gritty, gummy

thin strings, egg-white

stringy, clear

Mucus descriptions may be recorded in any manner you can fit them on the chart. Two examples are shown below.

Reminder

- Shininess on the tissue paper is not mucus. Mucus sits on the tissue paper and has substance.

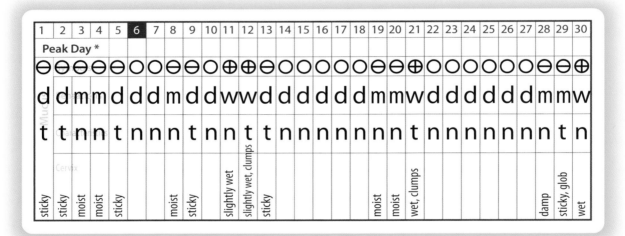

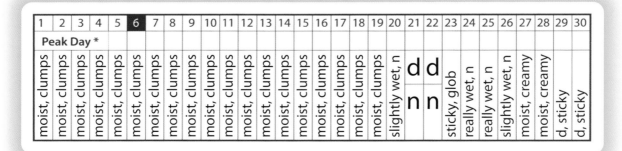

Next, you will learn how to identify and interpret each type of mucus pattern.

Patches

Mucus Patches are defined as *one or more days of mucus sensations/characteristics*. Any days with mucus sensations and/or mucus characteristics (less-fertile or more-fertile) are considered fertile. When one mucus patch is separated from another mucus patch by dry, nothing (d,n) days, there often is a time of infertility that can be considered a return to Phase I. This is determined by applying the Mucus Patch Rule.

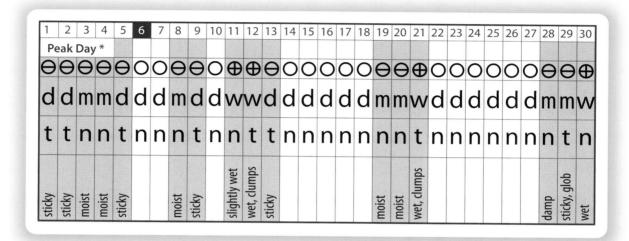

Mucus Patch Rule

Phase I infertility returns on the evening of the fourth day of dry, nothing after the last day of the mucus patch or non-menstrual bleed.

Conditions for Use:
• Breastfeeding
• No thermal shift

To interpret a mucus patch and apply the Mucus Patch Rule:

Mark the last day of the patch with a Δ (delta). Δ is a symbol that means change.

Number the dry, nothing days (d,n) following a Δ. After four d,n days (i.e., Δ1234), apply the Mucus Patch Rule to return to Phase I infertility.

The following example illustrates how to apply the Mucus Patch Rule when the mucus appears on and off in patches, in the absence of ovulation and a thermal shift. Phase I returns on the evening of Cycle Days 17 and 25. Follow the Phase I Guidelines.

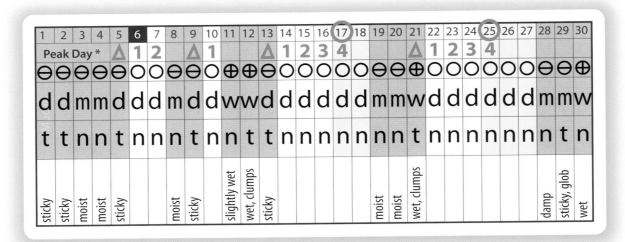

Reminder

- Mucus observations are made at the labia. Do not consider any mucus found internally during cervix checks, or what you may see in your underwear.

Notes

Mucus Patch Rule › Practice 1

If you are attending the Postpartum Class, you will complete this exercise in class. If you are using this Transitions Student Guide on your own, be sure to check your answers on pages 132–133 of the Appendix.

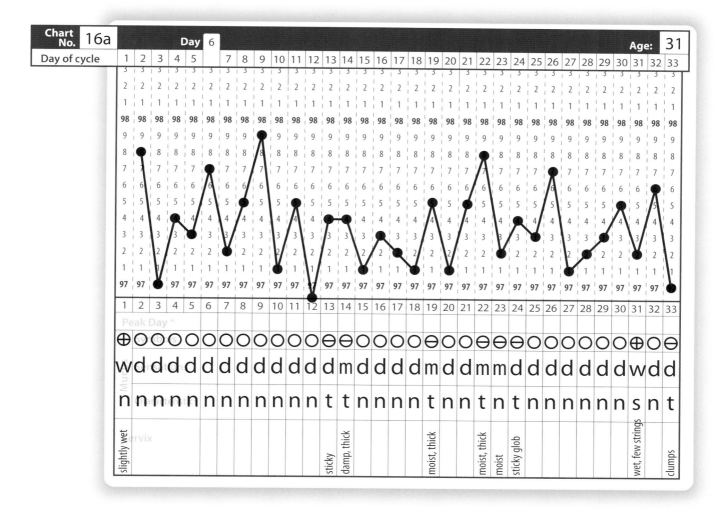

As you review this chart, try to mimic how you would actually approach its interpretation by looking at it day-by-day. In this example, a woman starts to chart as soon as she first notices mucus. On "Cycle Day 1" at the end of the day, she records a slightly wet sensation and a brief description. Although she knows that Phase II has begun, she does not yet know what type of mucus pattern this will be. So she continues to observe and record her mucus along with a brief description when mucus is present, and begins taking her temperature on Cycle Day 2.

Cover up all the days after Cycle Day 2 and then uncover them one day at a time. Continue to uncover each day until you can identify the pattern of mucus. Four days of dry, nothing are required in order to apply the Mucus Patch Rule. On Cycle Day 5, there are four days of dry, nothing and no thermal shift, so apply the Mucus Patch Rule. First label the last day of mucus (Cycle Day 1) with a Δ and then number the d, n days after. By the evening of the fourth day (Cycle Day 5), Phase I returns.

> Uncertain how to apply the Mucus Patch Rule? Contact your Teaching Couple or CCL.

Continue to uncover each day in like manner and apply the Mucus Patch Rule whenever possible. Note that sometimes a mucus patch will be followed by one, two, or three dry, nothing days, but not four. In these cases the Mucus Patch Rule cannot be applied, and Phase II will continue. Follow the Phase I Guidelines whenever Phase I returns.

To interpret this chart:

1. Mark the last day of each mucus patch with a Δ and number the dry, nothing mucus days that follow (i.e., Δ1234); review temperature pattern to ensure there is no thermal shift.

2. Apply the Mucus Patch Rule to determine the return to Phase I infertility. Draw a vertical phase division line through the temperature on the last day of Phase II and circle that day (because Phase I returns on the evening of that day). Indicate Phase I by writing the phase number "I" on the appropriate side of the vertical line, or mark a "1" on each cycle day.

3. When mucus returns, draw another vertical phase division line between the last day of Phase I and the first day of Phase II. Indicate Phase II by writing the phase number "II" on the appropriate side of the vertical line, or mark a "2" on each cycle day.

Reminder

- Draw phase division lines on your chart and indicate Phase I and Phase II.

Mucus with Bleeding

Women who breastfeed may frequently experience episodes of non-menstrual spotting/ bleeding. You learned previously that any non-menstrual spotting or bleeding is considered to be in Phase II because the bleeding could mask the presence of mucus. When non-menstrual bleeding ends, continue mucus observations. If mucus is observed, Phase II continues. If four dry, nothing days return, then the Mucus Patch Rule can be applied.

To interpret after a non-menstrual bleed ends, apply the Mucus Patch Rule:

Mark the last day of the non-menstrual bleed with a Δ.

Number the dry, nothing days (d,n) following a Δ. After four d,n days (i.e., Δ1234), apply the Mucus Patch Rule to return to Phase I infertility.

The next practice chart illustrates how to apply the Mucus Patch Rule when non-menstrual bleeding ends.

Notes

Mucus Patch Rule › Practice 2

If you are attending the Postpartum Class, you will complete this exercise in class. If you are using this Transitions Student Guide on your own, be sure to check your answers on pages 134–135 of the Appendix.

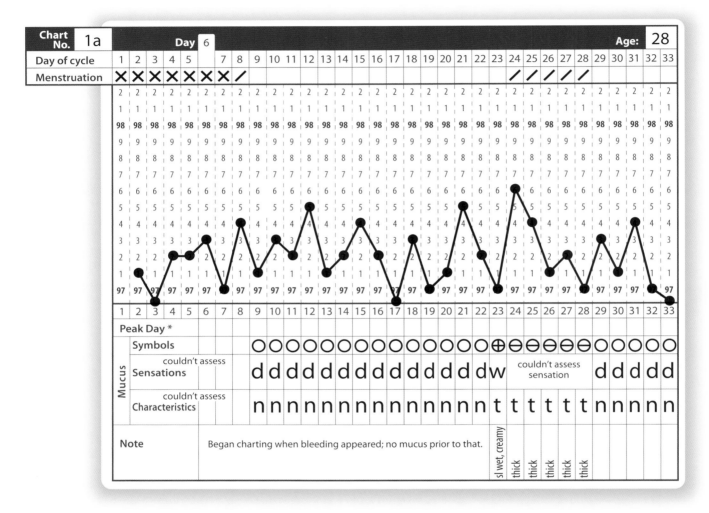

There are two instances of non-menstrual bleeding in this chart.

1. Mark the last day of each non-menstrual bleeding with a △ and number the dry, nothing mucus days that follow (i.e., △1234).

2. Apply the Mucus Patch Rule to determine the return to Phase I infertility. Draw a vertical phase division line through the temperature on the last day of Phase II and circle that day (because Phase I returns on the evening of that day). Indicate Phase I by writing the phase number "I" on the appropriate side of the vertical line, or mark a "1" on each cycle day.

3. When mucus or bleeding returns, draw another vertical phase division line between the last day of Phase I and the first day of Phase II. Indicate Phase II by writing the phase number "II" on the appropriate side of the vertical line, or mark a "2" on each cycle day.

When Mucus Follows Non-menstrual Bleeding

Non-menstrual bleeding sometimes occurs when the endometrium builds up so much that the top layer cannot be sustained solely by estrogen. As a result, the endometrium breaks down, and spotting or bleeding results. Mucus, therefore, may be present during and/or immediately after this bleeding episode.

To interpret a mucus patch following a non-menstrual bleed:

Mark the last day of mucus following the bleed with a Δ.

Number the dry, nothing days (d,n) following a Δ. After four d,n days (i.e., Δ1234), apply the Mucus Patch Rule to return to Phase I infertility.

Remember to follow the Phase I Guidelines.

The next practice exercise illustrates how to determine the fertile and infertile days when this situation occurs.

Notes

Mucus Patch Rule › Practice 3

If you are attending the Postpartum Class, you will complete this exercise in class. If you are using this Transitions Student Guide on your own, be sure to check your answers on pages 136–137 number of the Appendix.

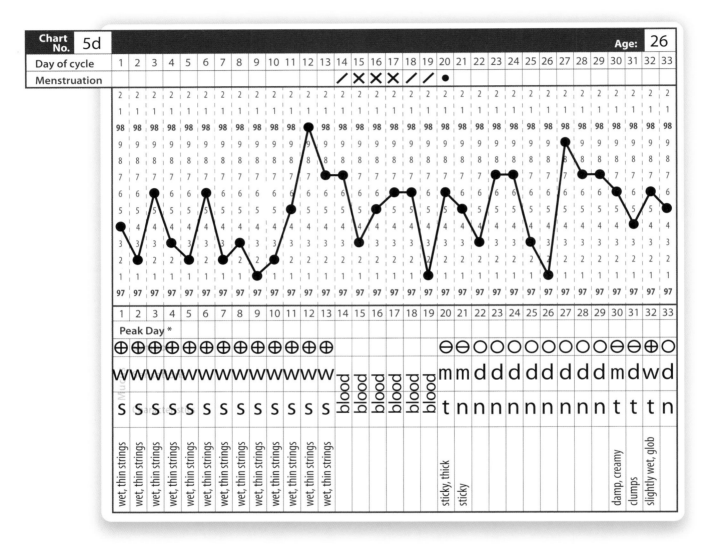

1. Mark the last day of mucus after the non-menstrual bleed with a Δ and number the dry, nothing mucus days that follow (i.e.,Δ1234). Label the last day of any other mucus patches with a Δ and number the d,n days that follow.

2. Apply the Mucus Patch Rule to determine the return to Phase I infertility. Draw a vertical phase division line through the temperature on the last day of Phase II and circle that day (because Phase I returns on the evening of that day). Indicate Phase I by writing the phase number "I" on the appropriate side of the vertical line, or mark a "1" on each cycle day.

3. When mucus or bleeding returns, draw another vertical phase division line between the last day of Phase I and the first day of Phase II. Indicate Phase II by writing the phase number "II" on the appropriate side of the vertical line, or mark a "2" on each cycle day.

Continuous Mucus

Another mucus pattern that mothers who breastfeed may experience is referred to as continuous mucus. Continuous mucus may manifest itself in two ways — unchanging or changing patterns.

Continuous mucus › unchanging pattern

Recall that in normal cycles, rising estrogen causes mucus to progress from less to more-fertile, ending with slippery, wet and/or stretchy mucus right before ovulation. During the postpartum time, however, the level of estrogen often *remains the same*. The amount of estrogen is sufficient to cause mucus, but since estrogen is in a "holding pattern" and not rising, the mucus remains the same and can be considered infertile after sufficient guidelines are met.

Basic Infertile Pattern

Drs. John and Evelyn Billings (founders of the World Organization of Method Billings) and James Brown, PhD, a reproductive biochemist, studied hormone levels and the patterns of mucus they produced. After much research, they determined that when an unchanging pattern of mucus occurs for 14 days during certain times like the postpartum or premenopause transitions, it can be considered infertile or Phase I. They coined the general phrase — **Basic Infertile Pattern (BIP)**.

> A Basic Infertile Pattern is an unchanging pattern of mucus that lasts for 14 days.

An unchanging mucus pattern might appear right after the lochia ends or later, and may remain for an extended period of time. At the onset of this mucus pattern you will not know that it is a BIP; therefore, initially it is considered Phase II. As you continue to write brief descriptions of your mucus, if it is a BIP you will notice that your descriptions remain the same day after day.

BIP Rule

Phase I infertility begins when a Basic Infertile Pattern is established and returns on the evening of the fourth day of return to the BIP.

Conditions for use

- Breastfeeding
- No thermal shift

After 14 days of unchanging mucus, you can apply the **Basic Infertile Pattern Rule**, and Phase I will begin that evening. Note the particular portion of the rule used to establish your BIP: **Phase I infertility begins when a Basic Infertile Pattern is established.**

Reminder

- A BIP is established on the evening of the 14th day of unchanging mucus.

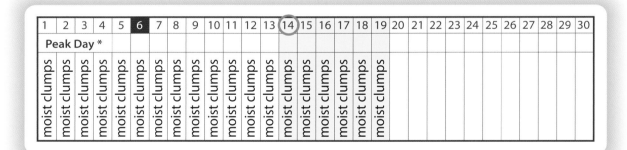

Changes to a Basic Infertile Pattern

Phase II returns with **any** change you observe in your BIP. Changes to your BIP occur when there is any change in any of the following:

- Sensations
- Characteristics
- Spotting/bleeding
- Quantity

Note that this change could be toward more-fertile mucus, toward less-fertile mucus, or a change within those categories. This is why descriptions of mucus are so important. Also note that you cannot look at a mucus symbol alone; mucus can change within sensations, characteristics or quantity. This signals a change from the BIP, but the symbol could be the same. The primary focus, therefore, should be on mucus descriptions during this time.

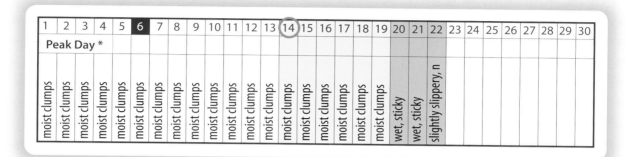

If the mucus changes back to the same infertile pattern, the BIP Rule can be applied to return to Phase I. The requirements for the return to Phase I are similar to the Mucus Patch Rule — four days are necessary, and in this situation, four days of return to the same BIP.

To determine when Phase I returns:

- **Mark the last day of change from the BIP with a Δ.** Δ refers to the last day of change from the BIP.

- **Number the BIP days that follow.** Phase I infertility returns on the evening of the 4th day of return to the BIP.

Remember to follow the Phase I Guidelines.

Phase	2	2	2	2	2	2	2	2	2	2	2	2	2	1	1	1	1	1	1	2	2	2	2	2	2	1	1	2	2	2
Day	1	2	3	4	5	6	7	8	9	10	11	12	13	14	15	16	17	18	19	20	21	22	23	24	25	26	27	28	29	30
Peak Day *																						Δ	1	2	3	4		Δ	1	2
Mucus	moist clumps	moist clumps	moist clumps	moist clumps	moist clumps	moist clumps	moist clumps	moist clumps	moist clumps	moist clumps	moist clumps	moist clumps	moist clumps	moist clumps	moist clumps	moist clumps	moist clumps	moist clumps	moist clumps	wet, sticky	wet, sticky	slightly slippery, n	moist clumps	moist clumps	moist clumps	moist clumps	moist clumps	wet	moist clumps	moist clumps

Note that it is also possible that once a woman has established the presence of a BIP, she may have only that one type of BIP during her transition time, or her infertile pattern could change from one type of BIP to another.

The next practice chart illustrates how to apply the Basic Infertile Pattern Rule, first to establish the BIP, and later to return to the BIP.

BIP › Practice 1

If you are attending the Postpartum Class, you will complete this exercise in class. If you are using this Transitions Student Guide on your own, be sure to check your answers on page 138 of the Appendix.

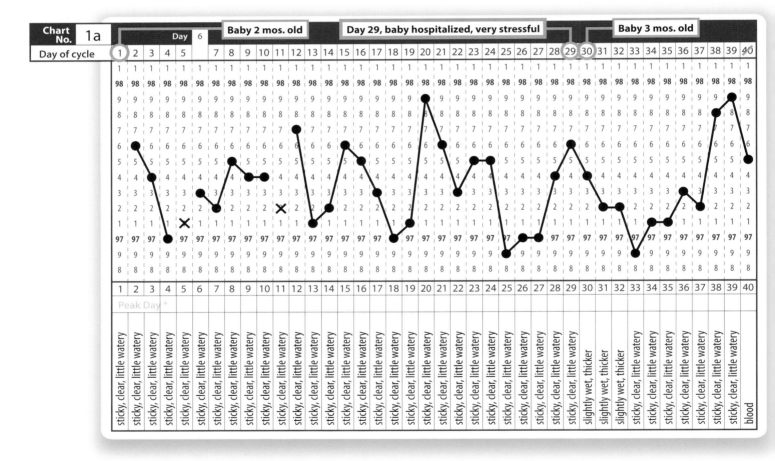

Review this breastfeeding mother's mucus descriptions. Note the age of her baby. Cover the chart data and then uncover them day-by-day. Ask yourself: "Is there a Basic Infertile Pattern?" If yes, then apply the BIP Rule to establish that an infertile pattern is present.

Remember that the first 13 days of an unchanging mucus pattern are considered Phase II. The 14th day of an unchanging pattern establishes the BIP, and Phase I returns that evening.

Next, are there any changes to the BIP? If yes, Phase II returns.

Last, is there a return to the infertile pattern? If yes, apply the BIP Rule.

1. Apply the Basic Infertile Pattern Rule to establish a BIP and the beginning of Phase I infertility.

2. To determine when Phase I returns, apply the BIP Rule and mark the last day of change from the BIP prior to the return to the infertile pattern with a Δ and number the BIP days that follow (i.e., $\Delta1234$).

3. Draw a vertical phase division line through the temperature on the last day of Phase II and circle that day (because Phase I returns on the evening of that day). Indicate Phase I by writing the phase number "I" on the appropriate side of the vertical line, or mark a "1" on each cycle day.

4. Draw a vertical phase division line between the last day of Phase I and the first day of Phase II. Indicate Phase II by writing the phase number "II" on the appropriate side of the vertical line, or mark a "2" on each cycle day.

Notes

BIP › Practice 2

If you are attending the Postpartum Class, you will complete this exercise in class. If you are using this Transitions Student Guide on your own, be sure to check your answers on page 139 of the Appendix.

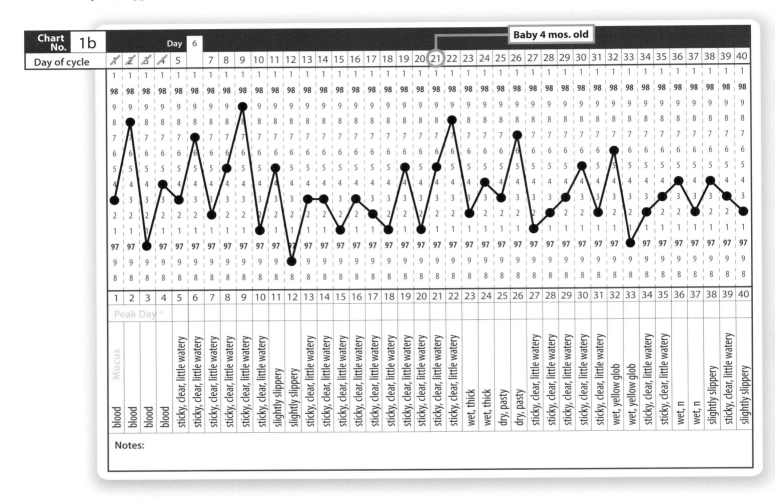

Practice Chart 2 is a continuation of the previous chart. Follow through with interpreting this chart using the same steps.

Reminder

- BIPs can change from one type to another type. Uncertain if you have a BIP? Contact your Teaching Couple or CCL.

Continuous mucus, changing pattern

During the postpartum transition, a second type of continuous mucus is a pattern that is **changing**. A changing mucus pattern is when the mucus sensations and/or characteristics change frequently enough that a Basic Infertile Pattern cannot be established. The pattern may also fail to disappear for any extended length of time. There may be an occasional day without mucus, but not four or more dry, nothing days to allow for the application of the Mucus Patch Rule. Common times to experience a changing mucus pattern while breastfeeding are:

When the baby is several months old and receiving complementary foods

This is a unique time for a mother. On the one hand, sufficient time has passed after childbirth that her ovaries may be trying to prepare for ovulation. On the other hand, the baby may be nursing frequently enough to prevent the ovaries from completely ripening a follicle for ovulation to occur. The end result is that mucus is observed almost daily, which can alternate from more- to less-fertile or vice versa. Because of this internal "tug-of-war," a relatively long pattern of changing mucus (i.e., six to eight weeks) may occur. Though the pattern of mucus changes, it does not progress from less-fertile to more-fertile mucus and then ovulation.

Notes

Note the example of a changing mucus pattern below. Compare that to the changing and progressing pattern of mucus that occurs with ovulation.

1	2	3	4	5	6	7	8	9	10	11	12	13	14	15	16	17	18	19	20	21	22	23	24	25	26	27	28	29	30
Peak Day *																													
⊕	⊖	⊕	⊖	O	⊖	⊕	⊕	⊖	⊕	⊕	⊖	O	⊖	⊕	O	⊕	⊕	⊖	⊕	O	O	⊖	⊖	O	⊖	⊖	O	⊖	⊕
w	m	w	s	l	d	m	w	w	d	s	l	s	l	d	d	m	m	w	d	s	l	s	l	m	m	w	d	d	m
t	t	n	t	n	t	t	t	t	s	t	t	n	t	t	s	n	t	n	t	t	t	n	n	t	t	n	n	t	n
wet, thick	sticky, thick	wet	slippery, milky		moist, clumps	wet, thick	wet, thick	sticky	slippery, thin strings	slippery, yellow glob	creamy		sticky, creamy	sticky, creamy	wet, egg-white		slippery, thick	slippery	damp, thick	damp, thick	wet, glob			damp, thick	thick		damp	sticky, glob	wet

Change in nursing

A changing pattern of mucus may also occur earlier during the postpartum transition if there is a dramatic change in the frequency of nursing. For instance, if a mother must pump milk for some time after childbirth instead of breastfeeding, her fertility signs may appear earlier. Her particular physiology and the frequency of the pumping may not be sufficient to delay the onset of fertility signs; thus, she may notice a changing pattern of mucus at that time. However, if the baby can return to breastfeeding full-time and pumping ceases, those fertility signs may disappear.

> Abstinence could be lengthy if you are trying to postpone pregnancy. Show your love in non-genital ways; be patient with one another.

Understand that this "tug-of-war" phenomenon does sometimes occur, but is very dependent on each woman's particular physiology and the frequency of suckling. For couples who have a serious reason to postpone pregnancy, it may require an extended period of abstinence. Pray together and support each other, and show your love in non-genital ways. This time will eventually end.

Continuous Discharge

Note that not all discharges are cervical mucus, and occasionally an unusual discharge may occur that is not related to fertility. For example, a strange discharge could be the result of an infection or underlying medical problem. If you have a discharge characterized by an odor and/or an unusual appearance, or something that is irritating or painful, contact your physician for an evaluation. (See the Reference Guide, Vaginal Discharges, in *The Art of Natural Family Planning® Student Guide*, pages 248–250.)

The three key measurable signs of fertility:

2. Temperature

During a normal fertility cycle, after ovulation the empty egg follicle becomes a structure called the corpus luteum, and it begins to produce progesterone. Progesterone causes your basal body temperature to rise, which begins the **luteal phase** — the number of days from the first day of temperature rise to the end of the cycle (last day before the next menstruation). When breastfeeding, however, there can be a significant period of time with no ovulations. If there is no ovulation, then there will also be no corpus luteum and no progesterone. Without progesterone, there will be no temperature rise.

> Temperatures may be erratic when breastfeeding, but they can be interpreted and used to determine when ovulation occurs.

Begin recording temperatures when you first detect mucus sensations, mucus characteristics, spotting or bleeding. In the absence of ovulation, though, temperatures often tend to be erratic. They frequently bounce up and down, and occasionally a few temperatures may actually rise and look similar to a thermal shift. If this happens, be sure to review your mucus pattern to verify whether or not you have had a changing pattern that gets more-fertile and then a dramatic change to a drying up pattern. When ovulation does finally occur, the temperature sign is the best way to verify it, in conjunction with Peak Day and a mucus dry-up pattern. Apply the ST Rule when able.

> Nighttime baby care normally will not interfere with the temperature sign.

Note: Many women are concerned that their temperature observations will be so disturbed by the nighttime care of their baby that this sign is not helpful during the transition. However, temperatures are usually not significantly affected by the routine care of a baby at night. It is good to note on your chart any unusual nighttime disturbances, such as being up for several hours with a sick baby, but know that a total of six hours of sleep at night — even with some interruptions — usually produces a basal temperature capable of being interpreted.

The three key measurable signs of fertility:

3. Cervix

As previously mentioned, the cervix is an optional sign. It indicates fertility when it is open and/or soft; it indicates infertility when it is both closed and hard.

Begin the cervix exam

- When you can resume marital relations as per your doctor's instructions AND
- When other observations indicate that fertility could be returning

Make cervix observations as explained in Lesson 2 — Review, and in Lesson 3 of *The Art of Natural Family Planning® Student Guide*.

Before having a baby, the shape of the cervical opening (os) is more rounded. After childbirth, you may notice changes. The opening may be more like a horizontal slit or a slit with curved ends, somewhat like a frown. However it feels, realize that this may constitute a new "baseline" for you when comparing its changes.

Note that when checking the cervix, you may occasionally detect mucus at the cervical os, or opening of the cervix. Mucus can change in its characteristics as it migrates from the os to the labia; in some cases, it never reaches the external labia. Furthermore, the clinical studies evaluating effectiveness have only examined external mucus observations. Therefore, only mucus found externally should be considered a sign of fertility. Any mucus found at the cervical os when checking the cervix can be ignored.

> Do not record any mucus observed at the cervical os.

Learning the cervix sign for the first time after having a baby may be challenging. Learners find it easiest to compare the cervix to how it feels in Phase III when it is closed and hard, but postpartum learners will not know what the cervix feels like in Phase III. If you would like to learn the cervix sign but are having difficulty during this transition, consider waiting until you begin ovulating. Then the Phase III infertile cervix will serve as a baseline for comparison of your cervix in Phases I and II of your next cycle.

If you are making the cervix observation, be sure to record this sign on the chart along with your mucus and temperature signs. Apply the ST Rule when possible.

Summary of Fertility Awareness when Breastfeeding

In summary, the steps to apply fertility awareness while you are breastfeeding are:

- Begin observing for mucus as soon as lochia lessens
- Observe and record mucus, temperatures and cervix (optional) when mucus or bleeding return
    - Assume Phase II fertility
    - Write brief descriptions of mucus
    - Identify mucus pattern
- Apply Mucus Patch or BIP Rules
- Apply the ST Rule when able

A flow diagram outlining Fertility Awareness during Breastfeeding can be found on page 151 of the Reference section.

Return of Fertility

When your ovulatory cycles return, initially, you may experience cycles that are longer than your pre-pregnancy cycles. In addition, you will likely have longer Phase IIs and shorter luteal phases. Such cycles are normal during the postpartum transition and to be expected. Your cycles will gradually shorten, and your luteal phases will gradually lengthen to your pre-pregnancy norms.

After you experience your first postpartum ovulation, your ovulatory cycles have returned and the Mucus Patch and BIP Rules no longer apply. Instead, you will go back to using the Day 5/6, Doering, and Last Dry Day Rules for Phase I, and the ST Rule for Phase III. Use your pre-pregnancy cycle history and earliest first day of temperature rise for the Day 5/6 Rule and Doering Rule respectively.

Notes

- After the first postpartum ovulation, your ovulatory cycles have returned and the Mucus Patch and BIP Rules no longer apply.

Postpartum Charting Hints

Number your charts

When you are postpartum and not yet experiencing normal, monthly ovulatory cycles, you may find the following numbering technique useful. It is especially helpful when your teachers or consultant reviews your charts.

If charting for the first time (i.e., are new to practicing NFP), label your first chart as 1a. Subsequent charts can be labeled as 1b, 1c, etc. until you ovulate. The chart following the first ovulation would be labeled as Chart 2. If you have charted your fertility signs prior to this, follow the number from your last chart when you conceived. For example, if it was 15, then number your postpartum charts as 16a, 16b, 16c, and so forth until you ovulate. The chart following your first ovulation would then be labeled 17.

Make notes on your chart

Continue using the Notes section of your chart to record significant events such as:

- the age or birth date of your baby
- how you are feeding him
- changes in nursing frequency
- sickness
- when solids are introduced

Continue charting on same chart

Remember that as your fertility returns, you will likely experience non-menstrual bleeds before your first ovulation. Therefore, do not start a new chart with the appearance of bleeding unless it has been preceded by a Peak Day, mucus dry-up and thermal shift. If not, continue charting on the same chart.

The next five charts illustrate the return of fertility after childbirth for a typical breastfeeding mother. In this example, the mother exclusively breastfed her baby for six months and continued to breastfeed adding only complementary foods over time.

Breastfeeding › Return of Fertility Chart 16a

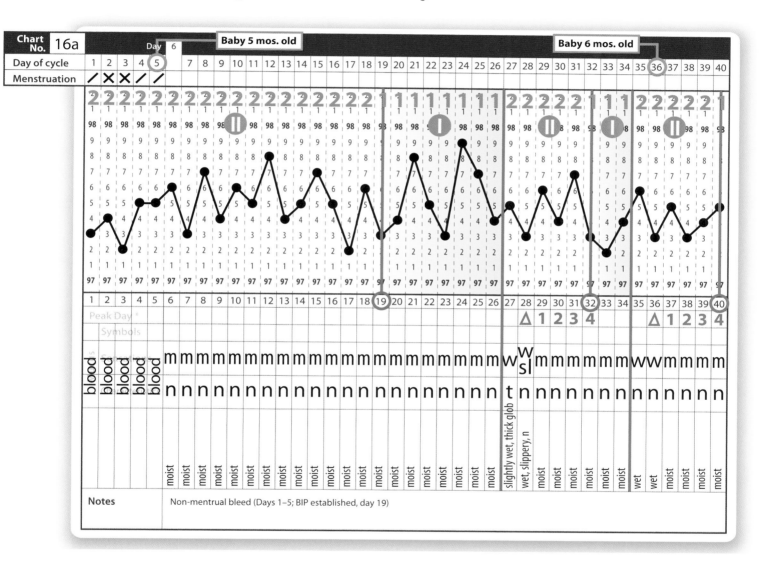

A breastfeeding woman experienced in NFP is on her 16th cycle (Chart 16a). Charting began at the first sign of fertility — a non-menstrual bleeding episode, i.e., there were no signs of mucus that preceded it. The chart includes the establishment of a BIP on Cycle Day 19 and several transitions going back and forth between Phase I and II through the application of the BIP Rule.

Breastfeeding › Return of Fertility Chart 16b

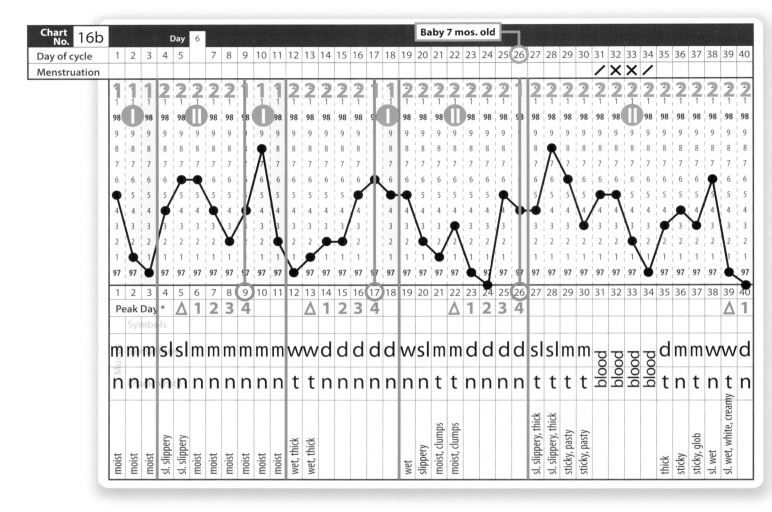

Chart 16b continues with alternating between Phase I and Phase II. First there is a change from her BIP of moist, nothing (Cycle Day 4) followed by a return to the BIP (Cycle Day 9). After that, however, the pattern of mucus changes in that she experiences mucus patches that are different from her BIP. Then, the Mucus Patch Rule can be applied (Cycle Days 17 and 26). Note also the non-menstrual bleed that occurs on Cycle Days 31–34.

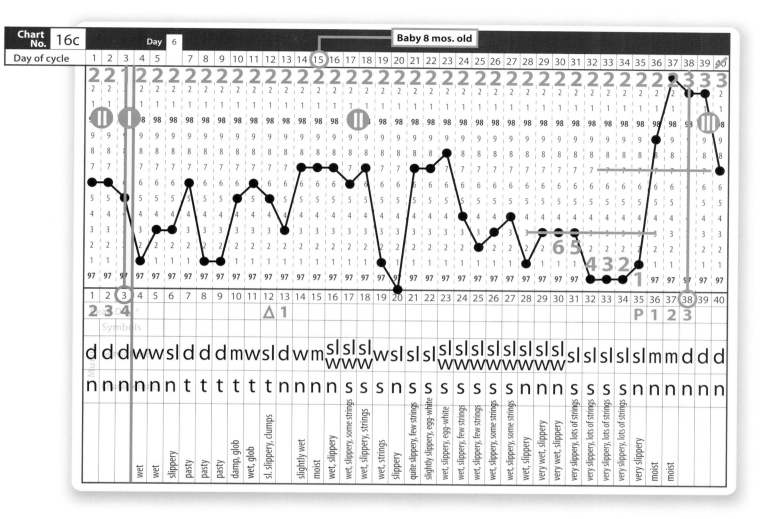

Chart 16c shows a long mucus patch culminating with Peak Day, a mucus dry up, and a thermal shift beginning on Cycle Day 36 with the application of the ST Rule. This chart also illustrates a short luteal phase (four days), which is typical for the first few postpartum ovulatory cycles. Note that over the course of the three charts in this series, the erratic temperatures stabilized and returned to a more normal pattern prior to the first ovulation. As a reminder, now that the first postpartum ovulation has occurred the Mucus Patch Rule and BIP Rule no longer apply.

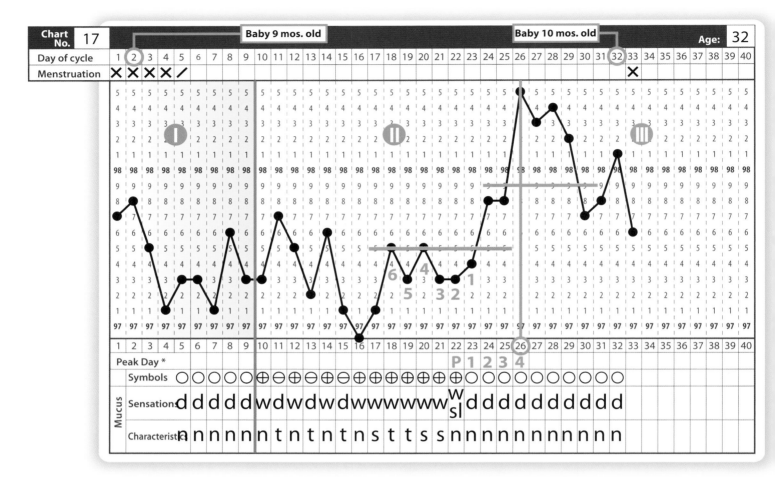

Chart 17 is the second postpartum ovulation with a longer luteal phase (nine days).

Breastfeeding › Return of Fertility Chart 18

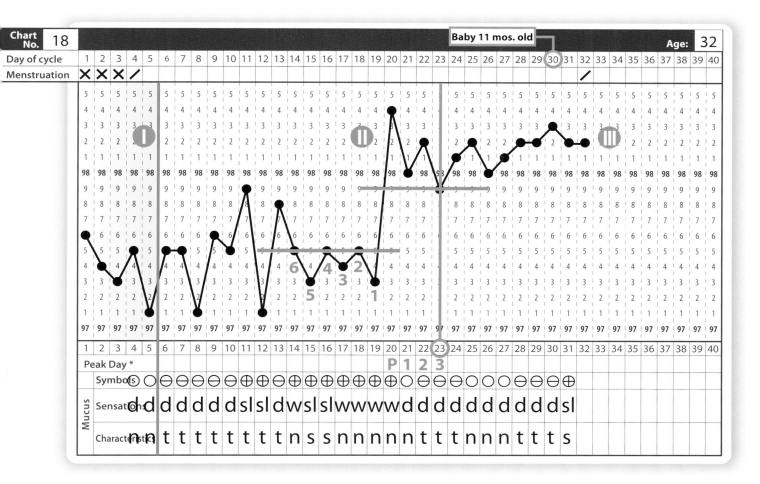

On Chart 18, Phase II is still somewhat longer than her normal pre-pregnancy cycles, but the luteal phase has returned to normal (12 days).

8 NFP, Responsible Parenthood and Marital Intimacy

Lesson 8

As you cradle your new baby in your arms and begin adjusting to your new roles as mom and dad, thoughts about welcoming the next child may be the farthest thing from your minds. It is good to remember that the call to practice responsible parenthood is ongoing — during times of normal fertility as well as during the postpartum transition. During the earlier weeks following childbirth, it is quite common to feel overwhelmed at the thought of another child. With time, healing, and recovery, however, these feelings can change. In reality, a woman's fertility may be many months — possibly even a year or more — away from returning. While this is primarily dependent upon the type of baby feeding, it is possible for any woman to experience an earlier-than-expected return of fertility. Therefore, ongoing prayers and discussions about family size are important and will empower and prepare you no matter when fertility returns — even if it happens while you are still in the throes of adjusting to the new little one in your arms now.

Responsible Parenthood

The birth of a baby rightly brings much change in a family's routine as the need to care for this newest family member becomes paramount. Husbands learn to be fathers, wives learn to be mothers, and both learn to relate to each other in new ways and with new perspectives. Add to this the practical considerations of starting a family, possibly adjusting to one income, moving to more appropriate housing, and more. If this baby is not the first, siblings also experience their own share of adjustment. Whew! It is easy to see the importance of being open with each other, praying together, and being in agreement about your responsible parenthood decisions at this time.

Recall that responsible parenthood is the virtuous decision to plan or to postpone another child. Responsible parenthood involves basing your family size decisions in love — love for God, love for your spouse, and love for the children you already have. The Catholic Church calls us to be generous by reminding us that children are the supreme gift of marriage. The Church has provided broad guidance regarding just reasons for responsibly postponing conception in *Humanae Vitae*, which speaks of "physical, economic, psychological, and social" conditions.[26] Note, however, that the Church does not define these conditions.

Thus, it is up to each married couple to prayerfully discern with a well-formed conscience whether the conditions in their marriage and family are appropriate or not for trying to conceive another child at any given time.

The time of postpartum infertility that most women experience with exclusive and continued breastfeeding usually allows ample opportunity for discernment as parents. When your fertility returns, are you both ready to welcome another child at that time? Are the two of you physically, economically, psychologically and socially ready to expand your family? Would it be prudent to postpone a pregnancy because one or more of your children requires additional attention that really should come from you? Does mom need more time to recover from a physically demanding pregnancy? Are we being selfish in postponing pregnancy? These are just a few examples of situations that may need to be carefully considered as you make decisions regarding family size. Many couples have found that these responsible parenthood decisions are made easier through exclusive and continued breastfeeding with its usual duration of delayed ovulation and extended infertility. This allows the baby to be nurtured on his/her timetable, while mother and father experience a natural spacing between children.

Regardless of the form of baby feeding, fertility will eventually return. If your prayerful discernment calls you to postpone the next pregnancy, NFP identifies the fertile and infertile times, allowing you to abstain or not, depending upon your circumstances. As the postpartum months continue, perhaps you find that a situation that initially caused you to rely on fertility awareness in order to delay a pregnancy changes. Perhaps now you could be more

---

[26] Pope Paul VI, *Humanae Vitae (On Human Life)*, no. 10.

open to another child. The beauty of NFP, even in the postpartum time, is that parents can change their minds from one "cycle" to another — from one day to another.

Balance is a key factor here as parents discern the needs of everyone in the family. Responsible parenthood is the virtuous and prudent decision to hope for another child, or to postpone or avoid conception for the good of the family. When a couple needs to postpone and they are beyond any natural infertility following childbirth, they can use their knowledge of fertility awareness to delay conception. This requires open and honest spousal communication, an art that is acquired through healthy marital intimacy.

Marital Intimacy

Intimacy involves the most private part of our being. **Marital intimacy** is much more than sexual intercourse; it involves both verbal and non-verbal communication about topics that are important to both spouses. This is especially important to keep in mind during these months of adjusting to new parenthood, which brings with it changes in the sexual relationship. In the midst of the excitement that surrounds the arrival of a new baby, it is also very important for you to set aside time to think, converse, pray, and just be together as husband and wife. It is not unusual for spouses to hit a few "bumps in the road" as they try to re-establish sexual intimacy following the birth of a new baby. Exhaustion, adjusting

to new roles, the effects of breastfeeding hormones, fear of another pregnancy… many such factors can influence a couple's sexual intimacy. But when we strive to keep our priorities in order — God, spouse, family, others — then we can be better lovers and better parents.

Marital intimacy takes on a deeper meaning when the newest member of the household is born and couples learn to re-order their priorities. Baby's needs come first as he cannot care for himself. Mom's and Dad's needs come second. A breastfeeding mother gives of herself to provide nourishment. A father must learn to give in other ways like caring for his wife, bathing, rocking, and walking the baby, caring for the other children, and doing more around the house. The postpartum household becomes an increasingly self-giving household. Marital intimacy when abstaining, however, is greatly enhanced when the new mother and father take on these selfless roles. A mother can know that she is being loved by the selfless acts performed by her husband, and a father can realize that his wife is caring for their child in the best way possible and that the baby's needs surpass his own for the present.

Perhaps this is best expressed in the words of author C. S. Lewis in *Letters of C. S. Lewis* (November 1952): "When I have learnt to love God better than my earthly dearest, I shall love my earthly dearest better than I do now. In so far as I learn to love my earthly dearest at the expense of God and instead of God, I shall be moving toward the state in which I shall not love my earthly dearest at all. When first things are put first, second things are not suppressed but increased."

Next Steps

The Couple to Couple League invites you to call or email for assistance when necessary. Don't wait if you need help. The best time to get assistance or support is when your fertility signs are first returning, but don't hesitate to call at any time. Contact your local CCL Teaching Couple, or if this is not possible, you may contact the CCL Central office directly at 1-800-745-8252, or ccli@ccli.org.

Part III — Premenopause

The Premenopause Woman • Fertility Awareness during Premenopause
What about Pregnancy? • Regarding Intimacy

The Premenopause Woman 9

Lesson 9

Many women feel a degree of uncertainty or possibly confusion as their fertile years gradually come to a close. They may wonder: "What will my transition to menopause be like? Will I have mood swings or hot flashes like my mother experienced? Will I have to worry about getting pregnant at a time in life when I don't feel capable of raising another child? Will I grieve because of the loss of my fertility? Will my husband still be attracted to me once I am no longer fertile?"

"The change of life is not the end of life."[27] However, it is a new stage of life, one in which a woman is no longer capable of having children. This change of life is known as **menopause** — officially, the cessation of menstrual periods for one year. On average, this occurs around the age of 51, but can occur earlier or later.[28]

The subject of this lesson is to acquaint you with some of the challenges and changes you may encounter in the years leading up to menopause, also known as **premenopause**. Further, this lesson will provide you with some underlying reasons for these changes, as well as help you identify when the special premenopause transition rules can be applied.

---

[27] Ingrid Hult Trobisch, *The Joy of Being a Woman...And What a Man Can Do* (New York: Harper & Row, 1975) 118.

[28] Fritz, M.A. and Speroff, L., *Clinical Gynecologic Endocrinology and Infertility*, 8th edition (Philadelphia: Lippincott Williams & Wilkens, 2011) 686.

Premenopause Challenges

During the fertile years, many women enjoy a high degree of regularity to their cycles. They may even be able to anticipate — to a degree — when mucus will begin, when ovulation will occur, and when menstruation will return. As the years go by, this regularity and knowledge of the cycle may make the practice of NFP easier. The downside we have seen, however, is that some couples develop poor charting habits. Because they know their cycles so well, they actually record fewer signs of fertility, and record them less often. Some couples even develop what can be referred to as a "calendar rhythm mindset." In other words, they are so used to, for example, Peak Day always being Day 15 or 16, or the basal temperature shooting up on Day 18, that they rely on those things happening instead of relying on the day-to-day signals their body is giving them. If the cycle stays the same, that thinking may not be problematic, but during premenopause there are noticeable changes in the menstrual cycle. These changes can sometimes be dramatic. Having a calendar rhythm mindset at a time when cycle irregularities become more commonplace will make the practice of NFP more difficult.

These charting challenges may also be accompanied by new symptoms some women experience during this transition time: mood swings, hot flashes, night sweats, brain fog, fatigue, insomnia, etc. Lastly, approaching permanent infertility may be a challenge for some, and even a time of grieving for the loss in their ability to have more children.

Underlying Reasons

When experiencing the symptoms of premenopause, some women feel like their reproductive system is actually "falling apart." It helps when women understand that there are reasons for all these cycle changes. Among the most important reasons are:

- Fewer and aging follicles
- Hormonal changes
- Less responsive reproductive tissues (i.e.,cervix, endometrium, cervical crypts)

Fewer & Aging Follicles

Women are born with a lifetime supply of ovarian follicles. As the years progress and a woman ages, the number of these follicles naturally declines. As the graph illustrates, the most rapid decline occurs when women reach their 40s.

Fewer & Aging Follicles

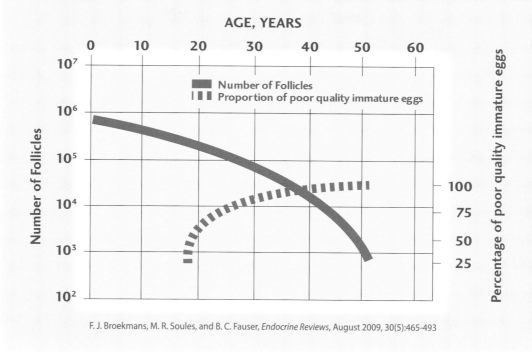

F. J. Broekmans, M. R. Soules, and B. C. Fauser, *Endocrine Reviews*, August 2009, 30(5):465-493

Not only does the number of follicles decline, but the remaining follicles may be less responsive to hormonal stimulation or be defective in some way that prevents normal maturation and release of an egg.

Hormonal changes

In the Review lesson you recalled how the four key reproductive hormones — follicle stimulating hormone (FSH), luteinizing hormone (LH), estrogen and progesterone — interact during a woman's most-fertile years. During premenopause, however, these hormones interact differently.

The pituitary gland releases FSH and LH during premenopause just as during the most-fertile years. But because older follicles may not respond to the stimulation of these hormones as well as they did when a woman was younger, FSH and LH levels increase and may remain high during cycles in the premenopause years.

During premenopause, ovulation does occur; but sometimes this happens prior to sufficient development of the follicle. When this happens, an immature egg is released that is incapable of being fertilized and/or the empty egg container becomes an inadequate corpus luteum that may produce a less than normal amount of progesterone.

As the premenopause transition progresses, fewer ovulations occur because the remaining follicles do not respond as well to FSH and LH stimulation. Fewer ovulations also mean fewer chances for a corpus luteum (empty follicle) to be formed, which in turn prevents progesterone production. Insufficient follicle development and/or fewer empty follicles cause a steady decline in progesterone. Note this in the graph.

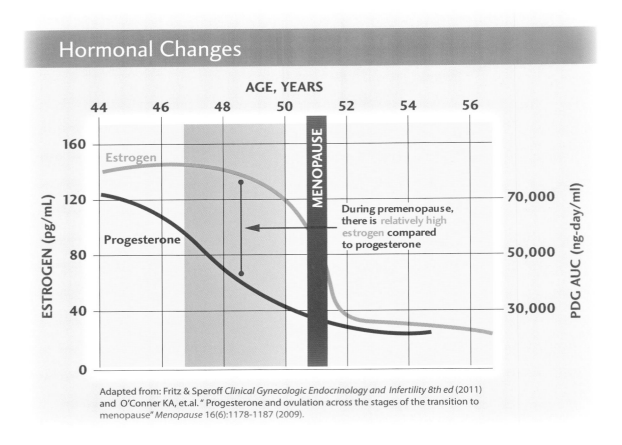

Hormonal Changes

Adapted from: Fritz & Speroff *Clinical Gynecologic Endocrinology and Infertility 8th ed* (2011) and O'Conner KA, et.al. " Progesterone and ovulation across the stages of the transition to menopause" *Menopause* 16(6):1178-1187 (2009).

Conversely, estrogen levels remain in the normal range, and may even rise somewhat in the premenopause years. Why does this occur? At times, the increased FSH and LH stimulation elicits higher estrogen production from the follicles, even though ovulation does not always result. Aging follicles are fickle and unpredictable, however. They may sometimes respond for a while, and then not respond, resulting in intermittent estrogen production. These fluctuations are considered normal.[29,30]

Outwardly, lower progesterone can cause cycles with a shorter luteal phase and/or a weak temperature rise. Outward signs of slightly elevated estrogen can be seen in longer episodes of mucus and/or **non-menstrual bleeding** (spotting or bleeding not preceded by a thermal shift). Fluctuating estrogen levels can produce "on and off" mucus patterns. Overall, the

[29] Fritz and Speroff, 682.
[30] O'Connor, K.A., et al., "Progesterone and ovulation across the stages of the transition to menopause," *Menopause* 16(6): 1178-1187 (2009).

steady decline in progesterone results in estrogen becoming the dominant hormone during most of the premenopause years. However, estrogen declines rapidly the last year prior to menopause. Once menopause is reached, FSH and LH remain high, whereas estrogen and progesterone remain low.

Less Responsive Tissues

At this time of life, the reproductive tissues age as well. The cervix, vagina, endometrium, and the cervical crypts that produce mucus may or may not respond to hormonal stimulation. Thus even if ovulation does occur, there may be little mucus present, and the cervix may not change or may not correspond with the mucus sign. The endometrium may build up more or less than normal, producing heavier or lighter than normal menstruations. Vaginal tissue thins and may become more easily irritated or feel dry.

All of these changes reflect overall biological aging which is yet another factor influencing the decrease in fertility. Note below how the relative fertility level declines as women age.

Reproductive Lifespan

Adapted from *Management of the Infertile Woman* (1988), *The Fertility Sourcebook* (2002), and Harlow, S.D., *JNAMS* 19(4) (2012).

A woman's ability to bear children is highest during her younger, fertile years. As premenopause begins, however, fertility dramatically decreases. Typically, this occurs when women are in their mid-40s, but it could begin earlier or later. On the graph, note the much more dramatic drop in fertility starting at age 40. Once menopause is reached, a woman is infertile for the rest of her life.

Defining the Start of Premenopause

When exactly does premenopause begin? Scientists from five countries and multiple disciplines agreed that cycle length variation is the most accurate marker to identify midlife stages of reproduction.[31] Accordingly, this lesson will define two different midlife stages of reproduction in the same manner: early premenopause and late premenopause.[32] You will see that once early premenopause is reached special rules apply. When the late stage arrives, you may have some idea about how long it will be before you reach menopause.

Early premenopause begins when there is a persistent difference of 7 days or more in the length of consecutive cycles, where "persistence" is defined as recurrence within 10 cycles of the first variable length cycle.[33] This does not include a cycle that may have been shortened or lengthened due to illness or stress of some kind. But if there is no obvious reason for your cycle length to have varied by 7 days or more, then note that as a possible indicator of early premenopause. If it happens again within the next 10 cycles, then early premenopause has begun. Early premenopause may actually last for a number of years. Cycles may remain rather regular in length with occasional shorter or longer cycles during this time. (Note the indication of early premenopause on the Reproductive Lifespan graph on the next page.)

It's also important to note that this definition of early premenopause focuses mainly on cycle length. A woman may experience other various cycle changes — differences in the mucus sign, bleeding patterns, thermal shifts — before significant cycle length variation sets in. These changes are reflective of the decreasing hormones and less responsive tissues, but they do not call for any changes in the application of NFP rules. The special transition rules are used after a woman has determined (using the following criteria) that she has reached early premenopause.

[31] Harlow, S.D., Ph.D., Gass, M., M.D., et al, "Executive Summary of the Stages of Reproductive Aging Workshop + 10: addressing the unfinished agenda of staging reproductive aging," *Menopause: The Journal of the North American Menopause Society* 19(4) (2012).

[32] Note that the term perimenopause is sometimes used to identify the late stage of premenopause. But perimenopause is often used interchangeably with premenopause as well. For simplicity, this text only uses the term premenopause to refer to the years leading up to menopause.

[33] Harlow and Gass, p.5.

Reproductive Lifespan

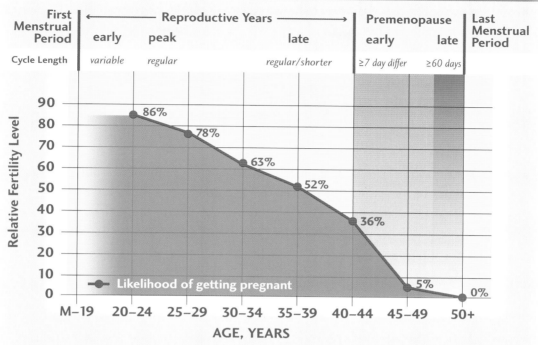

Adapted from *Management of the Infertile Woman* (1988), *The Fertility Sourcebook* (2002), and Harlow, S.D., *JNAMS* 19(4) (2012).

To establish when early premenopause begins, follow these steps:

1. List your cycle lengths of the last 10–12 cycles.

2. Calculate the difference between each.

3. Find the first cycle that is 7 days longer or shorter than its preceding cycle. This is your first indicator of possible early premenopause. *Exclude cycles influenced by stress, illness, etc.*

4. Determine if a second indicator has happened again within 10 cycles. If it has, you are in early premenopause. Note: Cycles used for the first indicator **cannot** be used as part of the second.

Reminder

- Early premenopause begins when there is a persistent difference of 7 days or more in the length of consecutive cycles, where "persistence" is defined as recurrence within 10 cycles of the first variable length cycle.

Review the following examples to illustrate this procedure:

On the left below, a 47-year-old woman's most recent 12 cycles began showing variability outside her historic normal range:

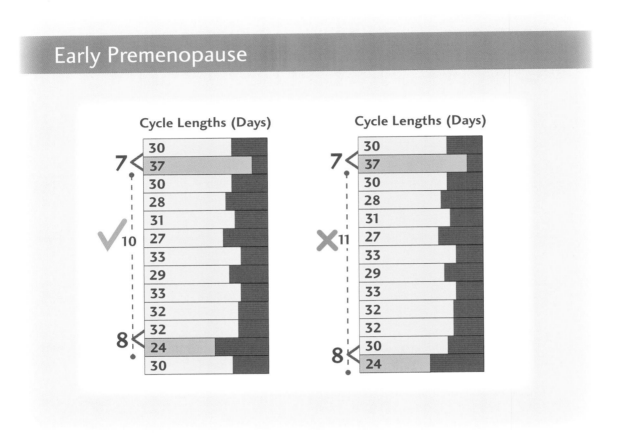

The second cycle is 7 days different in length from its preceding cycle (from 30 to 37 days). This is the first possible indicator of early premenopause. The next nine cycles that follow are of normal variability. The tenth cycle, however, is 8 days different (i.e., ≥ 7 days) from its preceding cycle, making it the second indicator of early premenopause. Since this second indicator occurred within 10 cycles of the first indicator, early premenopause has begun. (Note that the third cycle is also 7 days different, but is not a second indicator cycle since the second cycle was already used in the first calculation. In fact it indicates a return to normal cycle lengths.)

The example on the right is almost identical to the one on the left. The second cycle is again 7 days different in length from its preceding cycle, which is the first possible indicator of early premenopause. In this case, however, the second possible indicator occurs 11 cycles after the first, thus early premenopause has not yet started. Nevertheless the 24-day cycle is still an indicator cycle — it just did not occur within 10 cycles of the first indicator. This 24-day cycle can now be considered a "first indicator," and if another cycle length variation of 7 days or more occurs within 10 cycles of it, early premenopause will have started.

As you get older, you should continue to monitor your cycle lengths in this fashion to know when early premenopause begins and, therefore, when you can use the special transition rules.

Defining Late Premenopause

The **late** stage of premenopause begins when a woman experiences a cycle that lasts 60 days or more.[34] (Note this is indicated on the Reproductive Lifespan graph on page 81.) Usually menopause is reached within a couple of years of the beginning of late premenopause.

> Late premenopause begins when cycles are 60 days or longer.

And typically, this late stage is the time when the most physiological and cycle changes occur.

Cycle Changes Become the Norm

As mentioned earlier, you will notice various changes to your menstrual cycles during the transition to menopause, and many may happen before you reach the official stages of early or late premenopause. You may have longer cycles due to delayed ovulations. You could also experience shorter cycles as a result of a shortened luteal phase or earlier ovulation. Changes in "bleeding" or menstrual flow are also common. You may have longer periods in some cycles, or only a day or two of sparse bleeding or even just spotting in others. What's more, it is common to experience non-menstrual spotting/bleeding which can vary greatly in length and quantity of flow. Once in premenopause, these changes can occur at any time. It is only when you reach the defined stage of early premenopause that you can apply the special transition rules that are explained in the next lesson.

Fluctuating hormones also produce physical symptoms during this time. A number of these symptoms are addressed in the Reference section, pp. 156–159 under the title "Strategies for Good Health," including: hot flashes and night sweats, vaginal dryness, mood swings, anxiety, depression, weight gain, sleep problems, and problems with concentration and memory.

Notes

[34] Ibid., p. 5.

Fertility Awareness during Premenopause

Lesson 10

As you learned in the previous lesson, hormone levels during premenopause cause the signs of fertility to be different than they were during the early fertile years. Short luteal phases, weak temperature rises, and, in particular, on and off mucus become more commonplace. Instead of passing through Phases I, II and III in conjunction with ovulation, you will encounter days, weeks, and possibly even months in which you shift back and forth between Phase I infertility and Phase II fertility without ovulation. As ovulation becomes less frequent, so does the frequency of post-ovulatory Phase III. Thus fertility wanes from your most-fertile years, through the decreasing fertility of premenopause, and ultimately to the permanent infertility of menopause. Until that time arrives, you should continue observing, recording and interpreting your signs of fertility. Once early premenopause has been confirmed through cycle length variability, the Mucus Patch and Basic Infertile Pattern Rules can be used (explained later in this lesson).

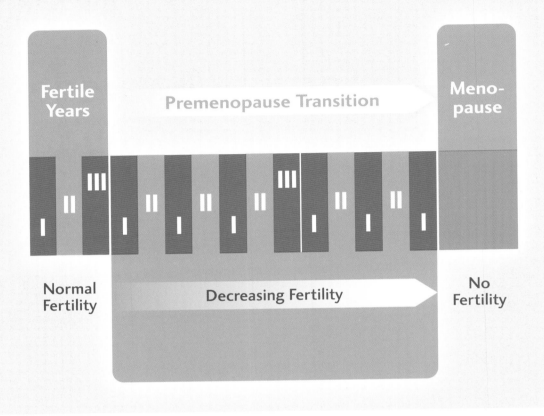

This lesson will examine the key measurable fertility signs — mucus, temperature and cervix —and explain how to interpret them. It is important to remember that detecting the start of mucus in a cycle is key.

The three key measurable signs of fertility:

1. Mucus

During premenopause, mucus may manifest itself differently than it did when you were younger; but you should observe it using the same techniques and diligently record it. As you were reminded in the Review lesson, at the start of each new cycle you should begin making mucus observations and following the Phase I Guidelines as soon as the menstrual flow decreases.

Reminder

• Observe and record mucus every day.

Phase I Guidelines

Evenings only: Remember that an infertile day is only determined after checking for mucus throughout the day; therefore, marital relations should be reserved for the evening. You may not notice any mucus during the day but then detect some mucus in the evening. If this occurs, consider yourself in Phase II because you detected mucus.

Not on consecutive days: Marital relations leave seminal residue in the vaginal area. If you detect this residue during your mucus checks the following day, the seminal residue could mask the presence of mucus. You cannot assume you are infertile unless you are sure that there is no mucus present. Therefore, you should abstain on any day that follows marital relations in Phase I unless you are experienced and can positively differentiate between seminal residue and mucus.

Phase II

Assume Phase II when mucus sensations or characteristics are detected. Since non-menstrual bleeding can also occur, this too is considered Phase II.

When longer cycles begin to occur, a woman may shift back and forth between Phase I and II because of hormonal fluctuations. How to interpret this "dance" between the fertile and infertile times is the subject of the rest of this lesson.

Mucus may vary during premenopause. It could be:

- Same as during most-fertile years
- Absent
- Present in different patterns
  — Patches
  — With non-menstrual spotting/bleeding
  — Continuous
    ◦ Unchanging
    ◦ Changing

When Mucus Is the Same as During the Most-fertile Years

If mucus signs are the same as during your most-fertile years, follow the standard steps for mucus interpretation that you have already learned. Note, however, that the number of days of mucus and/or the strength of the mucus sensations/characteristics may be less than what you experienced in the past.

- Mucus sensations and/or characteristics indicate the start of Phase II fertility

- Find Peak Day

- Apply the Sympto-Thermal Rule

In premenopause cycles, the number of mucus days may be fewer, and the strength of the mucus sensations/ characteristics may be less than in regular fertility cycles.

When Mucus Is Absent

Previously we reviewed that the absence of both mucus sensations and mucus characteristics indicates infertility. Therefore, if you have no mucus, consider yourself in Phase I infertility.

When Mucus Is Present In Different Patterns

The key to understanding why different patterns of mucus occur during premenopause is to recognize that they are directed by hormones. Remember that in the reproductive years, estrogen builds throughout the fertile time causing mucus to change from less-fertile to more-fertile. During premenopause, mucus still follows the level of estrogen but is manifested differently because ovulation may not be imminent. When the level of estrogen rises and then falls, mucus will appear and then disappear. If estrogen rises but then remains the same, mucus will appear and also stay about the same. Estrogen may rise sporadically causing a few random days of more-fertile mucus, but it does not continually rise. Thus, as estrogen rises and falls, mucus changes accordingly.

When estrogen rises and falls, mucus patterns follow.

To Identify Different Patterns of Mucus

To best assess how mucus changes during premenopause, you will need more detail than the broad descriptions (i.e., tacky, stretchy) and letters you use during regular fertility cycles. Therefore, you should write brief descriptions of your mucus sensations and characteristics. Be specific and avoid general terms like tacky or stretchy. Use any words that you think best describe what you are observing.

Reminder

- Mucus observations are made at the labia. Do not consider any mucus found internally during cervix checks or what you may see in your underwear.

At the end of each day's observations, compare today's observation with that of the previous day. If the mucus is about the same, use the same word(s) to describe it; if it differs, use a different word(s) to describe and record on the chart.

Assume Phase II fertility during this time.

Examples of brief descriptions

Sensations

slightly moist, moist

slightly damp, damp

slightly sticky, sticky

drippy, swampy

slightly slippery, slippery

very slippery, wet, watery, runny

Characteristics

sticky, big thick glob

small clumps

pasty, creamy, milky

gritty, gummy

thin strings, egg-white

stringy, clear

- Shininess on the tissue paper is not mucus. Mucus sits on the tissue paper and has substance.

Mucus descriptions may be recorded in any manner you can fit them on the chart. Two examples are shown below.

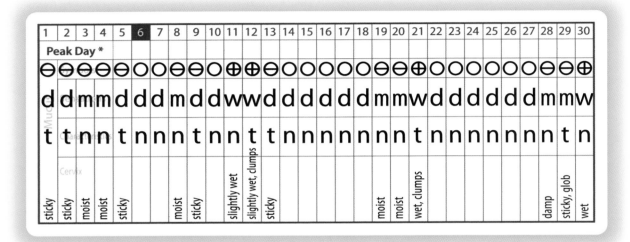

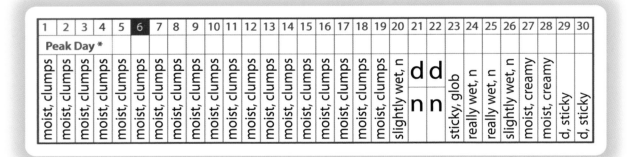

Next, you will learn how to identify and interpret each type of mucus pattern.

Patches

Mucus Patches are defined *as one or more days of mucus sensations/characteristics.* Any days with mucus sensations and/or mucus characteristics (less-fertile or more-fertile) are considered fertile. When one mucus patch is separated from another mucus patch by dry, nothing (d,n) days, there often is a time of infertility that can be considered a return to Phase I. This is determined by applying the Mucus Patch Rule.

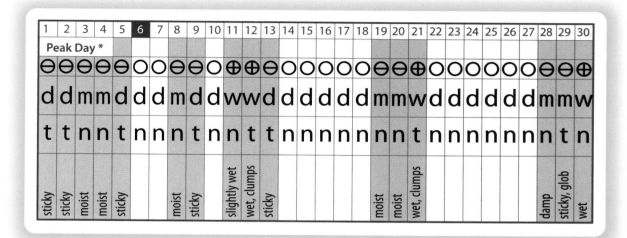

Mucus Patch Rule

Phase I infertility returns on the evening of the fourth day of dry, nothing after the last day of the mucus patch or non-menstrual bleed.

Conditions for Use:

- Premenopause
- No thermal shift

To interpret a mucus patch and apply the Mucus Patch Rule:

Mark the last day of the patch with a Δ (delta). Δ is a symbol that means change.

Number the dry, nothing days (d,n) following a Δ. After four d,n days (i.e., Δ1234), apply the Mucus Patch Rule to return to Phase I infertility.

The following example illustrates how to apply the Mucus Patch Rule when the mucus appears on and off in patches, in the absence of ovulation and a thermal shift. Phase I returns on the evening of Cycle Days 17 and 25. Follow the Phase I Guidelines.

Phase	2	2	2	2	2	2	2	2	2	2	2	2	2	2	2	2	2	1	1	2	2	2	2	2	2	1	1	1	2	2	2
	1	2	3	4	5	6	7	8	9	10	11	12	13	14	15	16	17	18	19	20	21	22	23	24	25	26	27	28	29	30
Peak Day *						△	1	2		△	1			△	1	2	3	4				△	1	2	3	4				
	⊖	⊖	⊖	⊖	⊖	○	○	○	⊖	⊖	○	⊕	⊕	⊖	○	○	○	○	○	○	⊖	⊖	⊕	○	○	○	○	○	○	○	○	⊖	⊖	⊕
	d	d	m	m	d		d	d	m	d	d	w	w	d	d	d	d	d	d	m	m	w	d	d	d	d	d	d	m	m	w
	t	t	n	n	t		n	n	t	n	n	t		t	n	n	n	n	n	n	n	t	n	n	n	n	n	n	n	t	n
	sticky	sticky	moist	moist	sticky			moist	sticky			slightly wet	wet, clumps	sticky							moist	moist	wet, clumps							damp	sticky, glob	wet

Notes

Mucus Patch Rule › Practice 1

If you are attending the Premenopause Class, you will complete this exercise in class. If you are using this Transitions Student Guide on your own, be sure to check your answers on pages 140–141 of the Appendix.

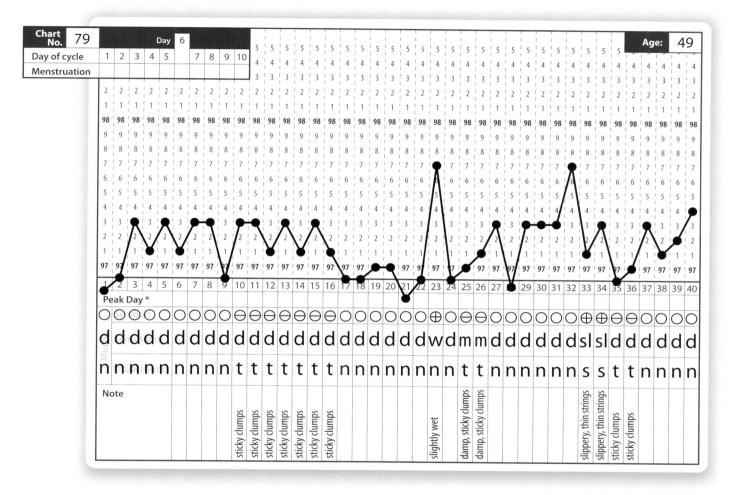

In this example, a 49-year-old woman has already confirmed that she is in the early stages of premenopause (based on previous cycle variability) and, therefore, can use the Mucus Patch Rule. Currently, she is experiencing a long cycle that has continued from her previous chart, and began noticing mucus on Cycle Day 10. Although she knew Phase II began when mucus first appeared, she did not yet know what type of mucus pattern this would be. So she continued to observe and record her mucus along with brief descriptions, and she continued to take her temperatures.

> Uncertain how to apply the Mucus Patch Rule? Contact your Teaching Couple or CCL Central.

As you review this chart, try to mimic how you would actually approach its interpretation by looking at it day-by-day. Cover up all the days after Cycle Day 9 and then uncover them one day at a time. Continue to uncover each day until you can identify the pattern of mucus. Four days of dry, nothing are required in order to apply the Mucus Patch Rule. On Cycle Day 20 there are four days of dry, nothing and no thermal shift, so apply the Mucus Patch Rule. First label the last day of mucus (Cycle Day 16) with a Δ and then number the d, n days after. By the evening of the fourth day (Cycle Day 20), Phase I returns.

Continue to uncover each day in like manner and apply the Mucus Patch Rule whenever possible. Note that sometimes a mucus patch will be followed by one, two, or three dry, nothing days, but not four. In these cases the Mucus Patch Rule cannot be applied, and Phase II will continue. Follow the Phase I Guidelines whenever Phase I returns.

To interpret this chart:

1. Mark the last day of each mucus patch with a Δ and number the dry, nothing mucus days that follow (i.e.,Δ1234); review the temperature pattern to ensure there is no thermal shift.

2. Apply the Mucus Patch Rule to determine the return to Phase I infertility. Draw a vertical phase division line through the temperature on the last day of Phase II and circle that day (because Phase I returns on the evening of that day). Indicate Phase I by writing the phase number "I" on the appropriate side of the vertical line, or mark a "1" on each cycle day.

3. When mucus returns, draw another vertical phase division line between the last day of Phase I and the first day of Phase II. Indicate Phase II by writing the phase number "II" on the appropriate side of the vertical line, or mark a "2" on each cycle day.

Reminder

• Draw phase division lines on your chart and indicate Phase I and Phase II.

Mucus with Bleeding

Women in premenopause typically experience non-menstrual spotting/bleeding. Some episodes of non-menstrual bleeding may even appear like a menstruation in both quantity and number of days of flow.

Non-menstrual bleeds may appear like menstruations; consider this time Phase II.

You learned previously that any non-menstrual bleeding is considered to be fertile (Phase II) because the bleeding could mask the presence of mucus. When non-menstrual bleeding ends, continue mucus observations. If mucus is observed, Phase II continues. If four dry, nothing days return, then the Mucus Patch Rule can be applied.

To interpret after a non-menstrual bleed ends:

Mark the last day of non-menstrual spotting/bleeding with a Δ.

Number the dry, nothing days (d,n) following a Δ. After four d,n days (i.e., Δ1234), apply the Mucus Patch Rule to return to Phase I infertility.

Follow Phase I Guidelines.

Reminder

- Do not start a new chart when a non-menstrual bleed occurs. Continue on the same chart.

When Mucus Follows Non-menstrual Bleeding

Non-menstrual bleeding sometimes occurs when the endometrium builds up so much that the top layer cannot be sustained solely by estrogen. As a result, the endometrium breaks down, and spotting or bleeding results. Mucus, therefore, may be present during and/or immediately after this bleeding episode.

To interpret a mucus patch following a non-menstrual bleed:

Mark the last day of mucus following the bleed with a Δ.

Number the dry, nothing days (d,n) following a Δ. After four d,n days (i.e., Δ1234), apply the Mucus Patch Rule to return to Phase I infertility.

Remember to follow the Phase I Guidelines.

The next practice exercise illustrates how to determine the fertile and infertile days when non-menstrual bleeding occurs.

Mucus Patch Rule › Practice 2

If you are attending the Premenopause Class, you will complete this exercise in class. If you are using this Transitions Student Guide on your own, be sure to check your answers on page 142 of the Appendix.

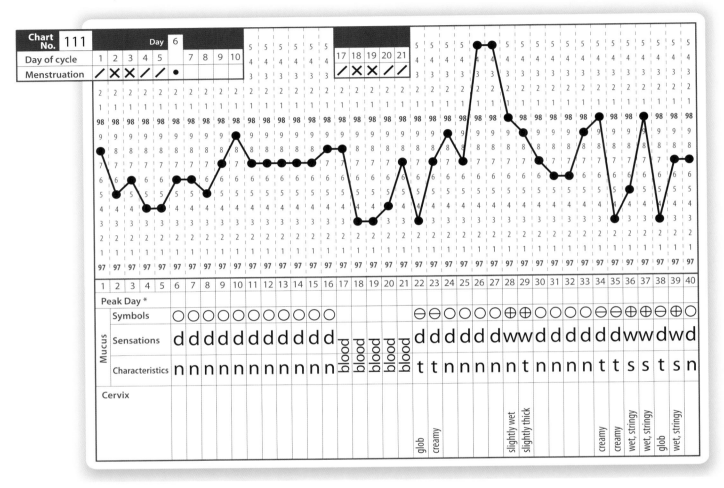

There are two instances of non-menstrual bleeding in this chart.

1. Mark the last day of the first non-menstrual bleed and the last day of the mucus following the second non-menstrual bleed with a Δ. Number the dry, nothing mucus days that follow (i.e., Δ1234). Label the last day of any other mucus patches with a Δ, and number the dry, nothing mucus days that follow.

2. Apply the Mucus Patch Rule to determine the return to Phase I infertility. Draw a vertical phase division line through the temperature on the last day of Phase II and circle that day (because Phase I returns on the evening of that day). Indicate Phase I by writing the phase number "I" on the appropriate side of the vertical line, or mark a "1" on each cycle day.

3. When mucus or bleeding returns, draw another vertical phase division line between the last day of Phase I and the first day of Phase II. Indicate Phase II by writing the phase number "II" on the appropriate side of the vertical line, or mark a "2" on each cycle day.

Continuous Mucus

Another mucus pattern that women may experience during premenopause is referred to as continuous mucus. Continuous mucus may manifest itself in two ways — unchanging or changing patterns.

Continuous mucus › unchanging pattern

Recall that in normal cycles, rising estrogen causes mucus to progress from less to more-fertile, ending with slippery, wet and/or stretchy mucus right before ovulation. During premenopause, however, the level of estrogen often *remains the same*. The amount of estrogen is sufficient to cause mucus, but since estrogen is in a "holding pattern" and not rising, the mucus remains the same and can be considered infertile after sufficient guidelines are met.

Basic Infertile Pattern

Drs. John and Evelyn Billings (founders of the World Organization of Method Billings) and James Brown, PhD, a reproductive biochemist, studied hormone levels and the patterns of mucus they produced. After much research, they determined that when an unchanging pattern of mucus occurs for 14 days during certain times like the postpartum or premenopause transitions, it can be considered infertile or Phase I. They coined the general phrase — **Basic Infertile Pattern (BIP)**. Once a women has established the presence of a BIP, she may have only that one type of BIP during her transition time, or her infertile pattern could change from one type of BIP to another.

> A Basic Infertile Pattern is an unchanging pattern of mucus that lasts for 14 days.

An unchanging mucus pattern may remain for an extended period of time. At the onset of this mucus pattern, you will not know that it is a BIP; therefore, initially, it is considered Phase II. As you continue to write brief descriptions of your mucus, if it is a BIP, you will notice that your descriptions remain the same day after day.

BIP Rule

Phase I infertility begins when a Basic Infertile Pattern is established and returns on the evening of the fourth day of return to the BIP.

Conditions for use

- Premenopause
- No thermal shift

After 14 days of unchanging mucus, you can apply the **Basic Infertile Pattern Rule**, and Phase I will begin that evening. Note the particular portion of the rule used to establish your BIP: **Phase I infertility begins when a Basic Infertile Pattern is established.**

Reminder

- A BIP is established on the evening of the 14th day of unchanging mucus.

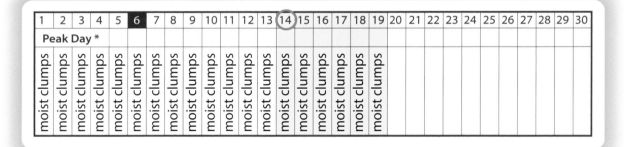

1	2	3	4	5	6	7	8	9	10	11	12	13	14	15	16	17	18	19	20	21	22	23	24	25	26	27	28	29	30
Peak Day *																													
moist clumps	moist clumps	moist clumps	moist clumps	moist clumps	moist clumps	moist clumps	moist clumps	moist clumps	moist clumps	moist clumps	moist clumps	moist clumps	moist clumps	moist clumps	moist clumps	moist clumps	moist clumps	moist clumps											

Notes

Changes to a Basic Infertile Pattern

Phase II returns with **any** change you observe in your BIP. Changes to your BIP occur when there is any change in any of the following:

- Sensations
- Characteristics
- Spotting/bleeding
- Quantity

Note that this change could be toward more-fertile mucus, toward less-fertile mucus, or a change within those categories. This is why descriptions of mucus are so important. Also note that you cannot look at a mucus symbol alone; mucus can change within sensations, characteristics or quantity. This signals a change from the BIP, but the symbol could be the same. The primary focus, therefore, should be on mucus descriptions during this time.

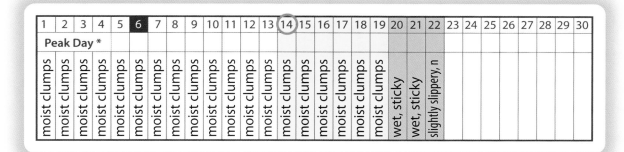

If the mucus changes back to the same infertile pattern, the BIP Rule can be applied to return to Phase I. The requirements for the return to Phase I are similar to the Mucus Patch Rule — four days are necessary and, in this situation, four days of return to the same BIP.

To determine when Phase I returns:

Mark the last day of change from the BIP with a Δ.

Number the BIP days that follow. Phase I infertility returns on the evening of the 4th day of return to the BIP.

Remember to follow the Phase I Guidelines.

Reminder

- BIPs can change from one type to another type. Uncertain if you have a BIP? Contact your Teaching Couple or CCL.

Phase	2	2	2	2	2	2	2	2	2	2	2	2	2	2	1	1	1	1	1	1	2	2	2	2	2	2	2	1	1	2	2	2
Day	1	2	3	4	5	6	7	8	9	10	11	12	13	(14)	15	16	17	18	19	20	21	22	23	24	25	(26)	27	28	29	30		
Peak Day *																						△	1	2	3	4		△	1	2		
	moist clumps	moist clumps	moist clumps	moist clumps	moist clumps	moist clumps	moist clumps	moist clumps	moist clumps	moist clumps	moist clumps	moist clumps	moist clumps	moist clumps	moist clumps	moist clumps	moist clumps	moist clumps	moist clumps	wet, sticky	wet, sticky	slightly slippery, n	moist clumps	moist clumps	moist clumps	moist clumps	moist clumps	wet	moist clumps	moist clumps		

The next practice chart illustrates how to apply the Basic Infertile Pattern Rule, first to establish the BIP, and later to return to the BIP.

Notes

BIP › Practice 1

If you are attending the Premenopause Class, you will complete this exercise in class. If you are using this Transitions Student Guide on your own, be sure to check your answers on page 143 of the Appendix.

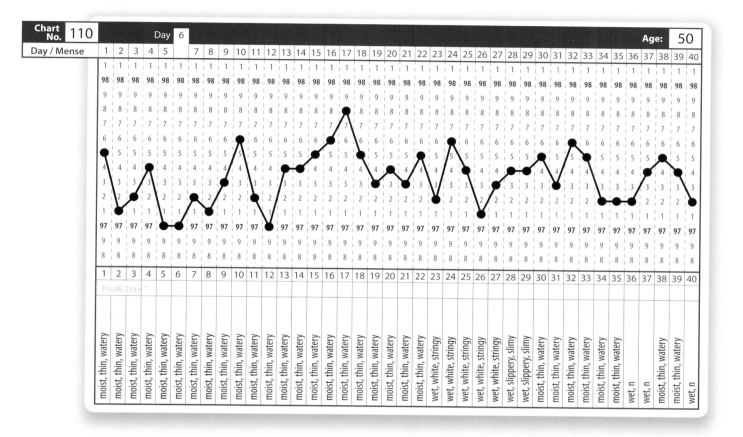

Review the mucus descriptions of this premenopausal woman. Hint: Cover the chart data and then uncover them day-by-day. Ask yourself, "Is there a Basic Infertile Pattern?" If yes, then apply the BIP Rule to establish that an infertile pattern is present.

Remember that the first 13 days of an unchanging mucus pattern are considered Phase II. The 14th day of an unchanging pattern establishes the BIP, and Phase I returns that evening.

Next, are there any changes to the BIP? If yes, Phase II returns.

Last, is there a return to the BIP? If yes, apply the BIP Rule.

1. Apply the Basic Infertile Pattern Rule to establish a BIP and the beginning of Phase I infertility.

2. To determine when Phase I returns, apply the BIP Rule and mark the last day of change from the BIP with a Δ and number the BIP days that follow (i.e., Δ1234).

3. Draw a vertical phase division line through the temperature on the last day of Phase II and circle that day (because Phase I returns on the evening of that day). Indicate Phase I by writing the phase number "I" on the appropriate side of the vertical line or mark a "1" on each cycle day.

4. Draw a vertical phase division line between the last day of Phase I and the first day of Phase II. Indicate Phase II by writing the phase number "II" on the appropriate side of the vertical line or mark a "2" on each cycle day.

BIP › Practice 2

If you are attending the Premenopause Class, you will complete this exercise in class. If you are using this Transitions Student Guide on your own, be sure to check your answers on page 144 of the Appendix.

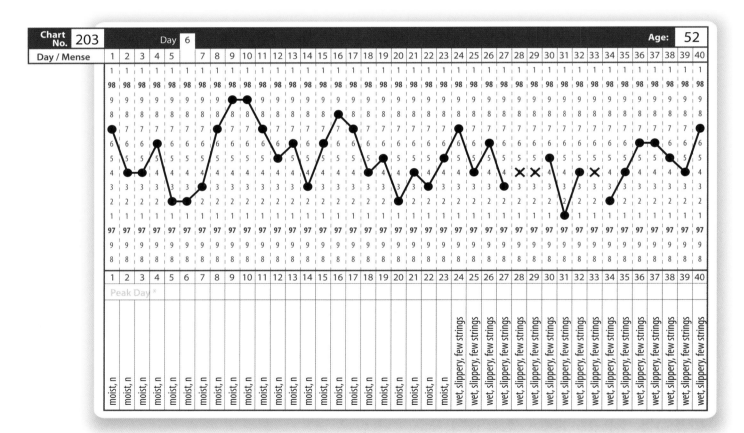

Practice Chart 2 is a chart from another woman in premenopause. Follow through with interpreting this chart using the same steps.

Hint: After a Basic Infertile Pattern has already been established, it is possible that after 14 days of a different, unchanging mucus pattern, a new BIP can be established.

BIP › Practice 3

If you are attending the Premenopause Class, you will complete this exercise in class. If you are using this Transitions Student Guide on your own, be sure to check your answers on pages 145–146 of the Appendix.

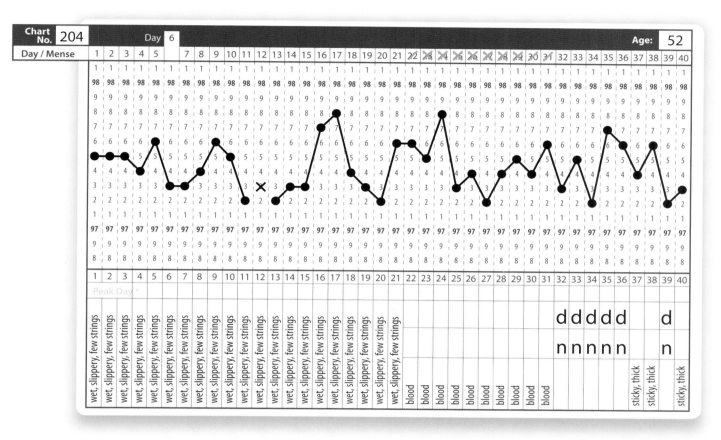

Practice Chart 3 is a continuation of the previous chart from the same woman in premenopause. Follow through with interpreting this chart using the same steps.

Continuous mucus › changing pattern

During premenopause, a second type of continuous mucus could be a pattern that is **changing**. A changing mucus pattern is when the mucus sensations and/or characteristics change frequently enough that a Basic Infertile Pattern cannot be established. The pattern may also fail to disappear for any extended length of time. There may be an occasional day

> With a changing pattern of mucus, abstinence could be lengthy if you are trying to postpone pregnancy. Show your love in non-genital ways; be patient with one another.

without mucus, but not four or more dry, nothing days to allow for the application of the Mucus Patch Rule. In these situations, a couple remains in Phase II since it could mean ovulation may happen soon. If ovulation does not happen soon, and a couple is trying to avoid pregnancy, there can be lengthy periods of abstinence.

Note the example of a changing pattern below. Compare that to the changing and progressing pattern of mucus that occurs with ovulation.

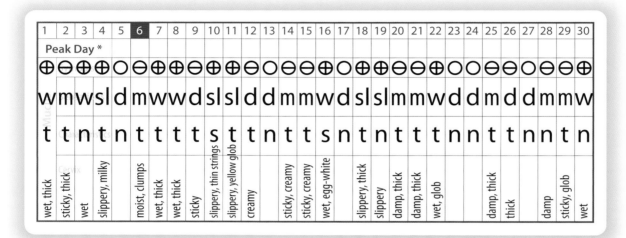

Continuous Discharge

Note that not all discharges are cervical mucus, and occasionally an unusual discharge may occur that is not related to fertility. For example, a strange discharge could be the result of an infection or underlying medical problem. If you have a discharge characterized by an odor and/or an unusual appearance or something that is irritating or painful, contact your physician for an evaluation. (See the Reference Guide, Vaginal Discharges, in *The Art of Natural Family Planning® Student Guide*, pages 248–250.)

Notes

The three key measurable signs of fertility:

2. Temperature

You will recall that during your most-fertile years, after ovulation the empty follicle becomes a structure called the corpus luteum which releases progesterone. The progesterone causes your basal body temperature to rise, beginning the **luteal phase** — measured by counting the days from the first day of temperature rise to the last day of the cycle. During premenopause, after ovulation it is possible to experience:

- Short luteal phase

- Long luteal phase

- Weak temperature rise, or delay in thermal shift in relationship to Peak Day

Since these post-ovulatory anomalies are typically due to poor progesterone production, the length of the luteal phase and strength of the temperature rise may vary.

Recall that temperatures prior to and just after ovulation are used to determine Phase III with the ST Rule. When fertility signs are present during years of normal fertility, it is assumed that ovulation will follow. Some women actually stop taking their temperatures once Phase III has been established. CCL recommends complete and accurate recordkeeping at all times to help interpret correctly. This is especially important during premenopause as the signs of fertility are waning. The temperature sign can be very helpful, as illustrated in the upcoming practice charts.

Short Luteal Phase

A cycle with a short luteal phase is interpreted the same as a regular cycle, but Phase III will be shorter than usual.

Short Luteal Phase > Practice

If you are attending the Premenopause Class, you will complete this exercise in class. If you are using this Transitions Student Guide on your own, be sure to check your answers on page 147 of the Appendix.

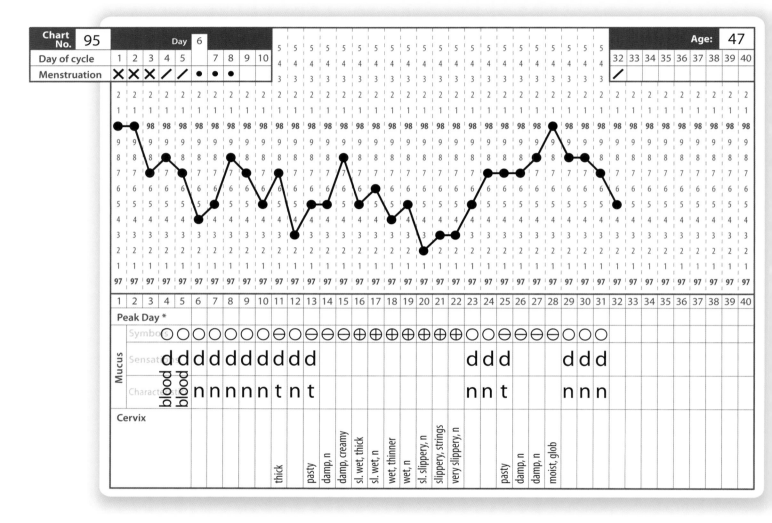

1. Draw a vertical line between the last day of Phase I and the first day of Phase II.

2. Mark the Peak Day and number the dry-up days that follow (i.e., P123).

3. Number the pre-shift six temperatures and draw horizontal lines indicating the LTL and HTL.

4. Apply the ST Rule, draw a vertical line through the temperature and circle that cycle day.

Long Luteal Phase

During premenopause, it is possible — although uncommon — to encounter a cycle with a long luteal phase. Usually a luteal phase of 21 days or more is a sign of pregnancy. In the absence of pregnancy, a possible explanation for a long luteal phase is when a developing follicle begins to produce progesterone without releasing its egg (**luteinized unruptured follicle**). When this happens a low amount of progesterone is typically produced, causing a weak temperature rise but longer than normal luteal phase. Since no egg is released, a cycle like this would be infertile.

This rare type of cycle anomaly usually ends in a bleeding episode, but not always. If bleeding does occur, start a new chart when it begins or, in the absence of a bleed, when temperatures drop to your normal pre-ovulatory levels. Remember, if you are unsure as to whether or not you may actually be pregnant, you can confirm it with a pregnancy test.

Notes

Long Luteal Phase › Practice

If you are attending the Premenopause Class, you will complete this exercise in class. If you are using this Transitions Student Guide on your own, be sure to check your answers on page 148 the Appendix.

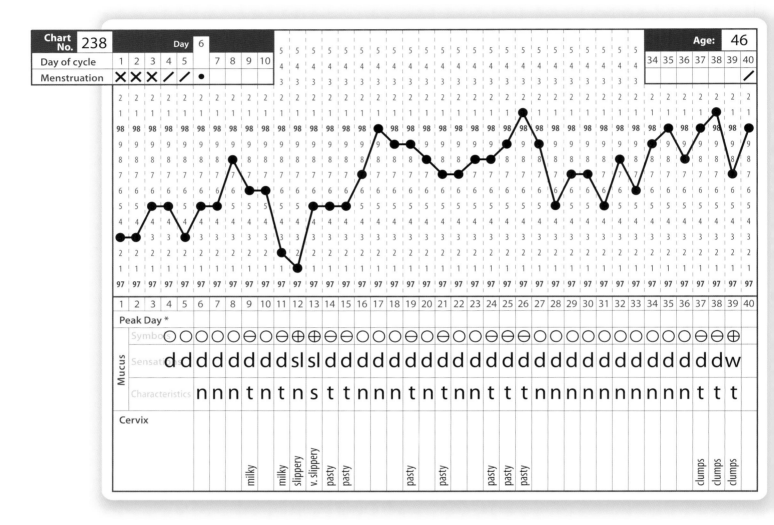

1. Draw a vertical line between the last day of Phase I and the first day of Phase II.

2. Mark the Peak Day and number the dry-up days that follow (i.e., P123).

3. Draw horizontal lines indicating the LTL and HTL.

4. Apply the ST Rule, draw a vertical line through the temperature and circle that cycle day.

Weak Temperature Rise or Delay in Temperature Rise

Sometimes the temperature rise (thermal shift) and luteal phase temperatures are shallow or weak with some dropping to or below the LTL. The general appearance of the temperature rise may be lower than during the more fertile years. In addition, the temperature sign may lag behind the other fertility signs delaying the application of the ST Rule. If any of these things happen or if you are having difficulty deciding if ovulation and a thermal shift have occurred, consider applying the Mucus Patch Rule or BIP Rule.

The following chart illustrates a cycle with what appears to be both a delay in the thermal shift and a weak temperature rise, all in one. Consider this chart to be yours. How would you approach it? Remember, you would not have the advantage of knowing ahead of time what your fertility signs are going to be later in the cycle. Therefore, you would have to approach this chart on a day-by-day basis. When the mucus disappears on Cycle Days 11–14, you also would not know that a delayed thermal shift was going to happen. As you review this chart, consider covering up all the data, and then uncovering it day-by-day to mimic how you would be analyzing your own chart.

Notes

Weak Temperature Rise or Delay in Temperature Rise › Example

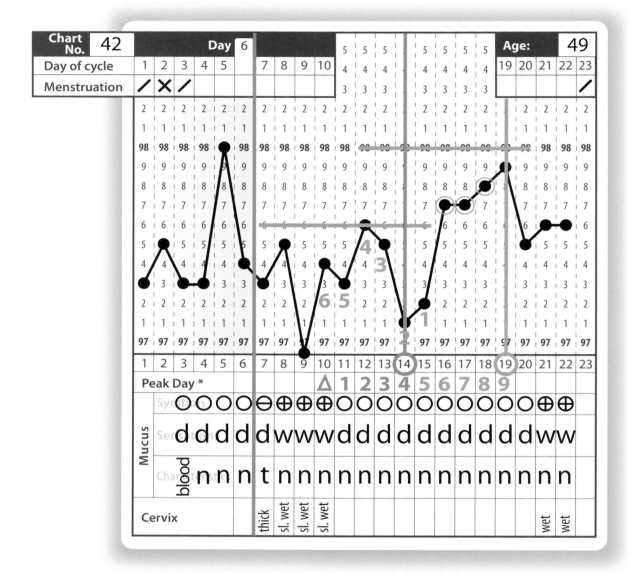

The end of Phase I according to:

Day 5/6 Rule = Unknown; if previous cycle history information was available, this could be determined

Doering Rule = Unknown; if previous earliest "first" day of temperature rise was known, this could be calculated

Last Dry Day = Cycle Day 6

Phase II begins: Cycle Day 7 because mucus is first observed on that day.

The analysis for the remainder of this chart is unique. Using day-by-day fertility awareness, note the four dry, nothing days on Cycle Days 11–14 that follow what could be a mucus patch. With no temperature shift, the Mucus Patch Rule could be applied and Phase I returns on Cycle Day 14.

Later, however, the temperatures do rise on Cycle Days 16–18, and by Cycle Day 19 the ST Rule can be applied. Phase III begins very late according to the ST Rule because of the lengthy delay in the thermal shift as compared to Peak Day. The luteal phase temperatures on Cycle Days 16–22 are shallow. None reach the HTL and three do not go above the LTL — all signs of low progesterone production.

Physiologically speaking, it is impossible to move from Phase I to Phase III, as was done when this chart was interpreted with the ST Rule after having first applied the Mucus Patch Rule. However, in premenopause, when you experience fertility signs that are not what you are accustomed to, applying the rules in a more unconventional manner may provide you with an interpretation. This could be preferable to waiting for an ovulation and normal thermal shift to occur, not knowing if that will even happen.

A key question: If this couple assumed infertility on Cycle Day 14 right before a thermal shift, what is the possibility of pregnancy? While we cannot know for sure, the possibility of pregnancy is likely very low. This woman is 49 years old. On Cycle Day 14, there is no mucus to keep sperm alive. Furthermore, since ovulation occurs most frequently on Peak Day or the day after, she is already four days past that and so would be infertile by Cycle Day 14. Lastly, the luteal phase of this cycle is only seven days long, which is probably insufficient to sustain pregnancy if it did occur.

The three key measurable signs of fertility:
3. Cervix

As you may recall from previous classes, the cervix observation is optional with regard to the Sympto-Thermal Method of NFP. However, this sign may be helpful during premenopause. It can add confidence, and it can help confirm a woman's fertility status if temperature and mucus signs do not coincide or appear confusing. The cervix sign may also reduce the number of days of abstinence when applying the ST Rule, especially in cases where the temperature rise is weak. On the other hand, since reproductive tissues do not respond the same as during the more fertile years, this may affect the cervix sign as well. Each woman is unique and, with experience, can determine to what degree the cervix sign may be helpful.

Cervix › Example

Chart No. 42 | **Day** 6 | **Age:** 49

Chart showing Day of cycle 1–23. Menstruation: / × / on days 1–3, and / on day 23. Temperature curve plotted (°F, 97–98+ scale). Peak Day row: P 1 2 3 4 5 6 7 8 9 (beginning day 11). Mucus Symbols, Sensation, Characteristic, and Cervix rows recorded below.

Mucus Sensation: d d d d w w w d d d d d d d d d d w w
Mucus Characteristic: blood n n t n n n n n n n n n n n n n n n
Cervix: h h h so so so so so h h h h h h h h h h h so

Returning to the previous example of a weak and delayed temperature rise, the cervix sign could have been helpful. In the application of both rules — the Mucus Patch Rule and the ST Rule — the cervix sign could have been another indicator of infertility (even though it is not required for either of the rules). With the cervix data added to the chart, there is a Phase III interpretation one day earlier than without it. Because the cervix was hard and closed on Cycle Days 16–18, Phase III began the evening of Cycle Day 18.

During premenopause, the key fertility signs may not always correlate with each other as well as they did when you were younger. That makes it even more important to continue observing and recording the signs of fertility — mucus, temperature and possibly even the cervix.

Other cycle variations

Early Mucus/Short Cycle

Occasionally during premenopause, ovulation can occur earlier in the cycle resulting in a shorter cycle. Cycles as short as 17–20 days are possible. Therefore, remember to check for mucus when menstruation decreases or lessens, or by Cycle Day 5, whichever comes first. When a shorter cycle is experienced, often the luteal phase is shorter as well.

> Mucus may appear during menstrual flow in very short cycles.

Note in the example below that mucus was observed on Cycle Day 4. This woman detected a slippery sensation when wiping on a day of heavier flow that was markedly different than the way her menstrual flow normally felt.

Should there be concerns over the possibility of pregnancy, especially if mucus begins to flow earlier? As you have already learned, women in premenopause are much less fertile than they were when they were younger. While pregnancy is possible, premenopause is a time of waning fertility. Also note that her luteal phase was only 9 days. A luteal phase less than 10 days

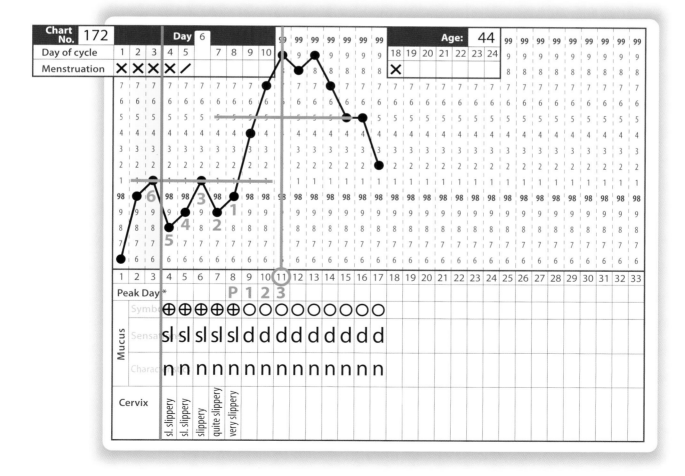

may be insufficient for implantation if pregnancy were to occur. Experience with detecting mucus during the later days of menstruation, combined with the fact that short cycles tend to have short luteal phases, should alleviate concern about getting pregnant.

Dry Cycle

Sometimes during premenopause there may be little to no mucus produced at all. In a "dry cycle," mucus is not present, even right before ovulation (near the pre-shift six temperatures). In the example, no mucus sensations or characteristics were detected throughout the entire cycle. There appears to be a thermal shift beginning on Cycle Day 19, however; and Phase III could be determined without mucus. The temperature on Cycle Day 21 drops back below the LTL, but Phase III could begin on the evening of Cycle Day 24 using the Temperature Only Rule.

> The absence of mucus means infertility.

Without any indication of mucus it is possible that ovulation (and thus Phase III) did not occur. In fact, another interpretation could be to extend Phase I all the way up to the bleeding episode beginning on Cycle Day 28. The bleeding would then be considered the fertile time as a non-menstrual bleed. When the bleeding stops, the Mucus Patch Rule would be applied.

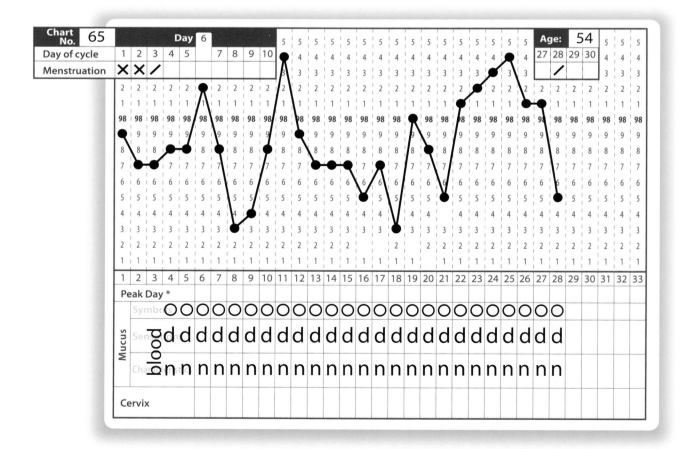

Similar to the Weak Temperature Rise chart shown earlier on page 112, the key question is: What is the chance of pregnancy? While there is always a "chance," sperm needs mucus to survive. Without mucus, combined with the woman's age of 54 and a possible short luteal phase, the chance of pregnancy is minimal.

What is important to note is that premenopause is a time of waning fertility, and anomalies such as these can sometimes occur. If at any time a couple has serious reasons to postpone pregnancy, they can choose to abstain.

One Day of Mucus

While a healthy buildup of mucus is expected during the normal reproductive years, it's possible in premenopause to have cycles with fewer days of mucus, and/or days when mucus is observed only one time. In this example, mucus was observed only once on one day (Cycle Day 20), which allows for the application of the Sympto-Thermal Rule by using that day as Peak Day. Applying the Last Dry Day Rule yields Cycle Day 19 as the last day of Phase I. Thus, in this unusual cycle there would be only 6 days of Phase II. Phase III starts on the evening of Cycle Day 25.

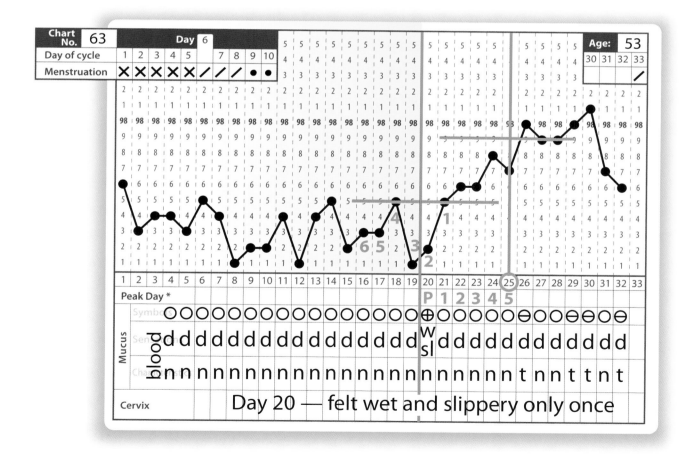

Summary of Fertility Awareness during Premenopause

For most women in their reproductive years, fertility comes and goes in cycles under the influence of several different hormones. There is a certain rhythmic regularity, and women who understand fertility awareness can observe and interpret their fertility signs readily during the various phases of their menstrual cycle.

Once you enter premenopause, the three phases of the cycle may begin to change their rhythm. Instead of experiencing Phase III infertility following Phase II fertility, you may now find yourself moving in and out of Phases I and II.

As you approach premenopause, continue observing and recording fertility signs and start tracking your cycle lengths more closely. Use the procedure outlined on page 83 to confirm you are in premenopause.

Once you reach premenopause,

- Write brief descriptions of your mucus
- Identify your mucus patterns
- Apply the Mucus Patch Rule or BIP Rule as appropriate
- Apply ST Rule when able

A flow diagram outlining Fertility Awareness during Premenopause can be found on page 155 of the Reference Guide. There are also some helpful charting tips in the postpartum section on page 64 that can be applied during premenopause as well, in particular, numbering charts for long cycles.

Two of the most important concerns expressed by women in premenopause are the possibility of pregnancy and the ability to remain healthy. The next lesson will address the topic of pregnancy, whereas, you will find information on maintaining good health during this transition time in the Reference section, pages 156–159.

Notes

What about Pregnancy? 11

Lesson 11

Can a woman in premenopause get pregnant? The answer is "Yes, but..." Although many women in their early forties are still capable of becoming pregnant, over time their fertility is greatly reduced. The degree of fertility and the age at which this happens varies from woman to woman. What is important to know is that women who are trying to achieve pregnancy, even after the age of 40, stand a better chance if they observe and record their fertility signs and use this knowledge to time marital relations.

Couples who are avoiding a pregnancy should be confident in their practice of NFP knowing that NFP remains highly effective. They should continue to chart and follow the rules and guidelines discussed in the previous lesson.

If you are trying to achieve a pregnancy, pre-conception preparation is important for both you and your husband. Good nutrition is a high priority; you should conscientiously improve your nutrition each year as you age. *The Art of Natural Family Planning® — Student Guide*, pp. 242–243, provides information on focused fertility awareness, maximizing sperm count, good nutrition and lifestyle habits, and fertility monitors. Other helpful resources may include: an NFP-friendly physician, *Fertility, Cycles & Nutrition* by Marilyn M. Shannon and, of course, focusing marital relations during the prime fertile times.

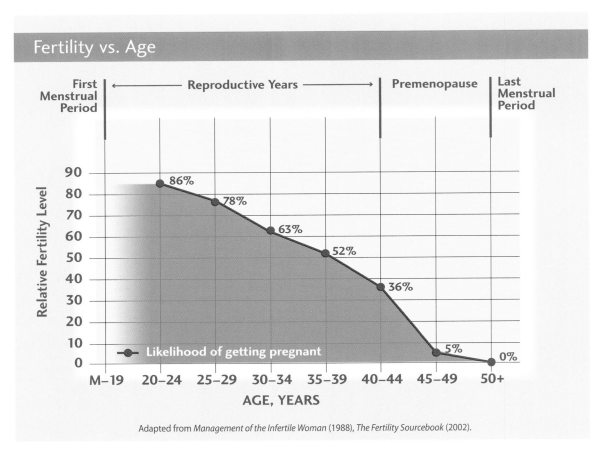

Fertility vs. Age

First Menstrual Period | ← Reproductive Years → | Premenopause | Last Menstrual Period

Relative Fertility Level

86%
78%
63%
52%
36%
5%
0%

Likelihood of getting pregnant

M–19 20–24 25–29 30–34 35–39 40–44 45–49 50+

AGE, YEARS

Adapted from *Management of the Infertile Woman* (1988), *The Fertility Sourcebook* (2002).

These considerations are especially important for couples who are hoping to achieve a pregnancy during premenopause. Abnormal FSH or LH levels before ovulation can cause

> Achieving pregnancy during premenopause may be more difficult.

the release of an immature egg at ovulation and/or the subsequent formation of a corpus luteum that releases insufficient progesterone, resulting in a short luteal phase and/or weak temperature rise. In this situation, pregnancy may be difficult to achieve. If it does occur, the new life may not be capable of normal development, or there may not be sufficient progesterone to sustain the preg-

nancy thus ending in a miscarriage.[35] During premenopause, there is a significant decline in the quality of the eggs, in the ability of the tubes to transport the eggs, and in the ability of the endometrium to nourish a fertilized egg.

This does not mean, however, that couples should automatically avoid pregnancy just because they have reached their forties. Many couples have successfully conceived at this age, and have even found that their babies help keep them young at heart. Discuss it as a couple, and prayerfully discern if you are being called to hope for a child at this time.

---

[35] Hilgers, Thomas W., M.D. *The Medical Surgical Practice of NaProTechnology*, Pope Paul VI Institute Press, Omaha, NE (2004), 770–780.

Regarding Intimacy 12

Lesson 12

There are many common mid-life events that sometimes give a negative connotation to the premenopause years, such as concerns about retirement, financial insecurity, separation from children, or caring for elderly relatives. These life occurrences are not caused by the change of life; rather, they develop simultaneously, but they can become intertwined with other adjustments and stresses during this time.

You have already learned the physiology behind premenopause and how to read your bodily signs of fertility and infertility during premenopause. This lesson will briefly discuss the topic of intimacy.

In the context of this lesson, intimacy involves much more than the physical act of sexual intercourse. Intimacy refers to having a strong couple relationship, developing a level of closeness and understanding that comes with strong communication. Whether you are in the transition years of premenopause or have entered the post-reproductive stage of menopause, spousal intimacy should be nurtured. It involves both verbal and non-verbal communication about things that are important to both husband and wife. For some couples, either husbands and/or wives, part of this communication relates also to acknowledging the onset of permanent infertility and how that will impact their relationship. Communication can be enhanced by spending quality and quantity time together through activities like taking walks, developing or renewing shared interests, and maintaining regular "date nights," all of which can help keep your spouse as a priority. Such outward manifestations of a couple's love are often powerful witnesses to younger couples. While marital intimacy may begin in the early years of marriage, its richness continues to evolve and deepen as spouses mature in their "coupleness" over a period of time.

With regard to a decrease in sexual intimacy in aging women, culture and attitude are more influential than are nature and physiology. "The two most important influences on older sexual interactions are the strength of the relationship and the physical condition"[36] of each spouse.

In addition to the various symptoms of premenopause mentioned in Lesson 9, some women may experience circumstances that could make sexual intimacy difficult. When a woman is in her forties, **androgens** (male hormones produced by the adrenal glands) become more prominent as estrogen declines. Normally, this will increase a woman's sexual desire; however, if the adrenal glands are exhausted or are not functioning properly, a woman may have a lower desire for sexual intimacy. In addition, weak pelvic floor muscles can interfere with sexual climax; the Kegel exercise[37] can help to strengthen these muscles and can also benefit the bladder.

In her chapter on menopause in *The Joy of Being a Woman*, Ingrid Trobisch uses a husband's description of his wife to illustrate the depth of intimacy that enabled him to "read" his wife through her physical expressions and through the wrinkles on her face.

"Dr. (Theodor) Bovet in *A Handbook to Marriage* relates a touching story about his wife after many years of marriage. Once while gazing upon his sleeping wife, he took notice of the different character lines in her countenance. She was not old, but she had some wrinkles in her face. The little wrinkles above her eyebrows appeared whenever she asked a witty question. When thinking deeply, she wrinkled the middle of her brow causing vertical lines in her forehead. The deeper horizontal wrinkles were etched in her forehead when he was sick and she was worried about their future. He noticed the wrinkles at the corners of her eyes which radiated love

---

[36] Fritz and Speroff, 687-688.

[37] Shannon, "Nutrition and Womanly Desire," *Family Foundations*, November-December 2004, The Couple to Couple League. You can practice this exercise by contracting the muscles that would stop you from urinating. This can be done for several seconds about 25 to 50 times a day to increase the tone of these muscles.

when looking at their child. At the corner of her mouth were little wrinkles which appeared whenever she noticed a funny animal. She would laughingly say, 'Our Lord God certainly had a sense of humor that he would create such a comical animal.' The more intently he gazed upon her face, the memories of their years together swept over him and he saw into her very being. Indeed, her precious face contained in shorthand her whole biography."[38]

The Couple to Couple League is about couples, and it is fitting to close this lesson on premenopause by considering the husband and the changes in his reproductive function as time goes on. What can the two of you expect? In men, of course, there is no obvious "change of life" as there is in women. Many older men with younger wives have fathered children. But the male hormone testosterone gradually and steadily declines with age, which can affect both sexual desire and sexual function. Other changes in the function of the various reproductive organs can sometimes affect erection and ejaculation, even when sexual desire remains normal. There are morally-licit drugs which can improve the age-related decline in sexual ability. Good nutrition, exercise, and stress reduction, as well as natural remedies available over-the-counter, can also help with these issues while improving every aspect of a man's overall health. See the chapter entitled "Men's Fertility and Reproductive Health" in *Fertility, Cycles & Nutrition* for more information on this topic.

Far beyond nutrition, exercise and stress reduction is the relationship between husband and wife. "Enjoy life with the wife whom you love, all the days of the fleeting life that is granted you under the sun" (Eccles. 9:9).

What next?

The Couple to Couple League invites you to call or email for assistance when necessary. Don't wait if you need help. The best time to get assistance or support is when you first are unsure about how to interpret your fertility signs, but don't hesitate to call at any time. Contact your local CCL Teaching Couple, or if this is not possible you may contact the CCL Central office directly at 1-800-745-8252.

---

[38] Trobisch, 119.

Supplemental Material

Appendix • Reference Guide • Glossary • Index

Appendix: Answers to Practice Charts

Steps for Applying the Sympto-Thermal Rule

1. Find Peak Day and number the three days of drying-up after it from left to right.

2. Close to Peak Day, find three temperatures that are higher than six preceding temperatures.

3. Number the pre-shift six from right to left.

4. Draw the Low Temperature Level (LTL) on the highest of the pre-shift six temperatures.

5. Draw the High Temperature Level (HTL) at 0.4° F above the LTL.

6. Find the third of three normal post-peak temperatures that are all above the LTL ("post-peak" means temperatures occurring after Peak Day). If this third temperature is at or above the HTL, Phase III begins on the evening of that day.

7. If the third normal post-peak temperature does not reach the HTL, check the cervix sign (if recorded). If there are three days of a closed, hard cervix, then it is not necessary for the third normal post-peak temperature to reach the HTL. Phase III begins on the evening of that day.

8. If the requirements in steps #6 and #7 are not met, wait for an additional normal post-peak temperature above the LTL; Phase III begins that evening.

9. After you apply the ST Rule and determine the start of Phase III, draw a vertical phase division line through the temperature dot on the first day of Phase III.

Notes

Review > Practice Chart (page 15)

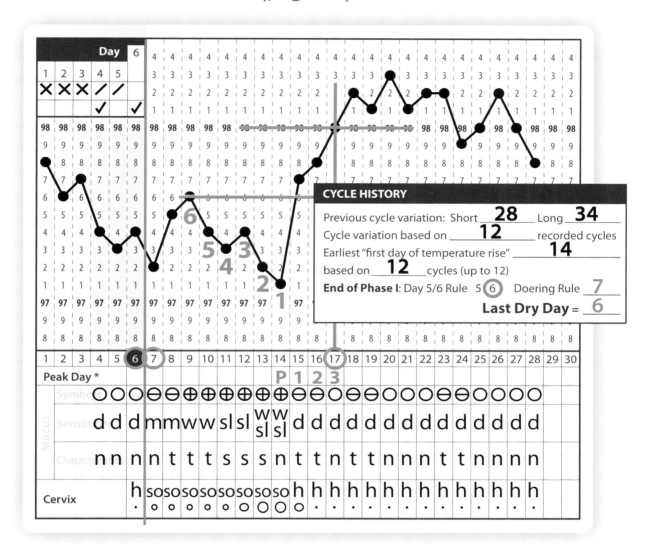

Mucus observations began as soon as menstrual flow decreased, which was on Cycle Day 4 of this chart; this is important in determining the infertility of days of lesser menstrual flow.

Phase I and II:

- Day 5/6 Rule = Cycle Day 6
- Doering Rule = Cycle Day 7 (although it is not reached because mucus is present)
- Last Dry Day Rule = Cycle Day 6
- Latest day of Phase I = Cycle Day 6

Phase III:

Since Peak Day is Cycle Day 14, the third day of drying up past Peak Day is Cycle Day 17, and the three normal post-peak temperatures above the LTL are Cycle Days 15, 16 and 17. The third of these temperatures (Cycle Day 17) is at (or above) the HTL. Thus, Phase III begins on the evening of Cycle Day 17.

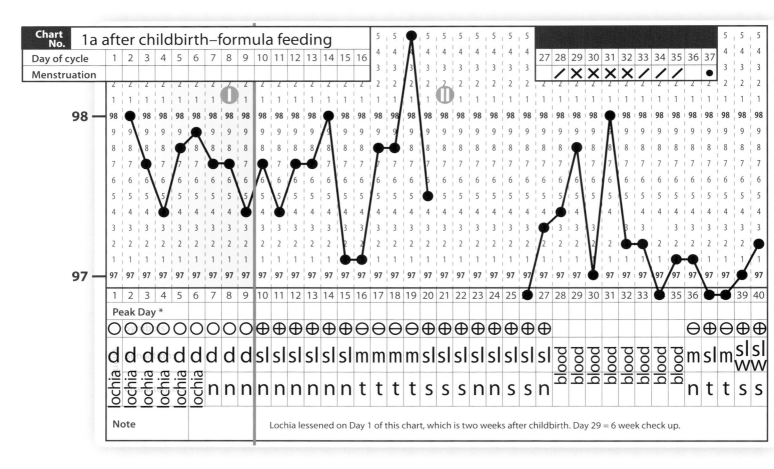

Phase I and Phase II:

- Day 5/6 Rule = Not applicable
- Doering Rule = Not applicable
- Last Dry Day = Cycle Day 9
- End of Phase I = Cycle Day 9

Charting began when lochia lessened, two weeks after childbirth. While Phase I lasted through Cycle Day 9, it is unlikely that this woman would have been cleared by her doctor to resume marital relations by then.

Phase II began on Cycle Day 10 when mucus was detected, and continued through the end of this chart (and into her next chart), which is not unusual for the first full cycle after childbirth. When formula feeding, once Phase II begins it continues until Phase III can be determined, even if an occasional dry, nothing day is experienced.

Phase III:

Not applicable since there is no thermal shift.

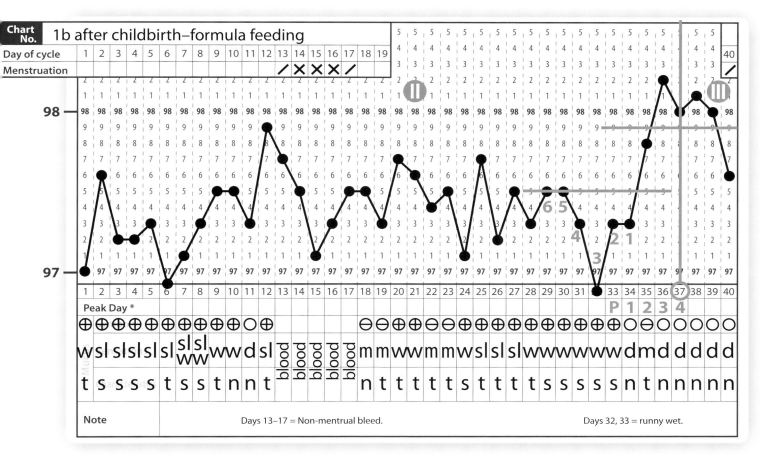

Phase I and Phase II:

- Day 5/6 Rule = Not applicable
- Doering Rule = Not applicable
- Last Dry Day = Not applicable
- End of Phase I = Not applicable

This chart is a continuation of the previous chart. Phase I does not apply because once Phase II begins, it continues until Phase III can be determined.

Phase III:

Since Peak Day is Cycle Day 33, the third day of drying up past Peak Day is Cycle Day 36 and the three normal post-peak temperatures above the LTL are Cycle Days 35, 36 and 37. The third of these temperatures (Cycle Day 37) is at (or above) the HTL. Thus, Phase III begins on the evening of Cycle Day 37.

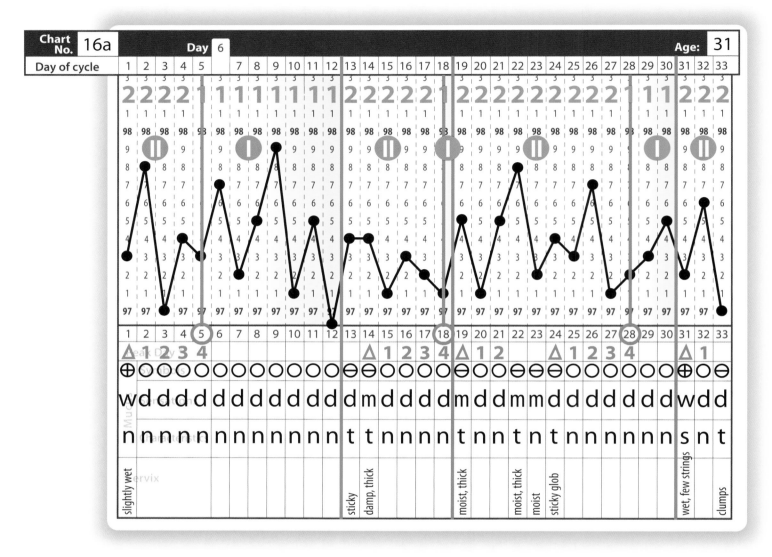

Phase I and II:

Phase I returns on Cycle Days 5, 18 and 28. Phase I infertility returns on the evening of the fourth day of dry, nothing (Cycle Days 5, 18 and 28), after the last day of the mucus patch (Cycle Days 1, 14 and 24) or non-menstrual bleed.

Charting and brief descriptions of mucus began when mucus was observed, and thus Phase II fertility began as well. The Day 5/6, Doering and Last Dry Day Rules do not apply in a postpartum situation with no cycling. However, after four days without mucus (d,n) the Mucus Patch Rule can be applied to return to Phase I infertility.

Mark the last day of each mucus patch on Cycle Days 1, 14, 19, 24 and 31 with a Δ. Number all d,n days after accordingly (i.e., 1234), and apply the Mucus Patch Rule on Cycle Days 5, 18 and 28.

Phase I Guidelines apply.

Phase III:

Not applicable since there is no thermal shift.

Notes

Chart No.	1a		Day	6																											Age:	28
Day of cycle	1	2	3	4	5		7	8	9	10	11	12	13	14	15	16	17	18	19	20	21	22	23	24	25	26	27	28	29	30	31	32	33
Menstruation	✕	✕	✕	✕	✕	✕	✕	╱																╱	╱	╱	╱	╱					

	1	2	3	4	5	6	7	8	9	10	11	12	13	14	15	16	17	18	19	20	21	22	23	24	25	26	27	28	29	30	31	32	33
Peak Day *								△	1	2	3	4												△	1	2	3	4					
Mucus — Symbols								○	○	○	○	○	○	○	○	○	○	○	○	○	○	○	⊕	⊖	⊖	⊖	⊖	⊖	○	○	○	○	○
Mucus — Sensations (couldn't assess)								d	d	d	d	d	d	d	d	d	d	d	d	d	d	w	couldn't assess sensation						d	d	d	d	d
Mucus — Characteristics (couldn't assess)								n	n	n	n	n	n	n	n	n	n	n	n	n	n	n	t	t	t	t	t	t	n	n	n	n	n

Note: Began charting when bleeding appeared; no mucus prior to that.

Notes under Phase II (Cycle Days 23–28): sl wet, creamy; thick; thick; thick; thick; thick

Phase I and II:

Phase I returns on Cycle Days 12 and 32. Phase I infertility returns on the evening of the fourth day of dry, nothing (Cycle Days 12 and 32) after the last day of the mucus patch or non-menstrual bleed (Cycle Days 8 and 28).

The bleeding episodes on Cycle Days 1–8 and 24–28 are non-menstrual bleeds. The bleed that begins on Cycle Day 1 is the first sign of fertility since mucus was not observed prior to that point. Mucus was first observed and brief descriptions were recorded on Cycle Day 23. This marks the beginning of Phase II again, and is then followed by another non-menstrual bleed. These days are considered to be a potentially fertile time. Mark the last day of the bleeds on Cycle Days 8 and 28 with a △. Number the d,n days after accordingly (i.e., 1234). Apply the Mucus Patch Rule on Cycle Days 12 and 32.

Realize that a bleeding may appear like menstruation in quantity/number of days of flow; but this does not verify whether it is a menstruation or not. Ovulation with a thermal shift that precedes a bleeding episode confirms that the bleeding is a menstruation. Both mucus patches and non-menstrual bleeds can be experienced while breastfeeding before the first ovulation returns.

Phase I Guidelines apply.

Phase III:

Not applicable since there is no thermal shift.

Notes

Mucus Patch Rule > Practice 3 (page 52)

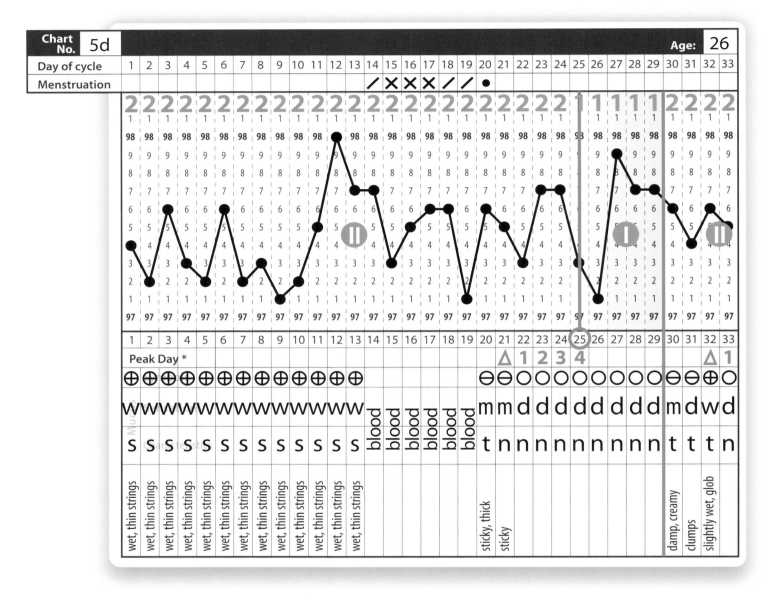

Phase I and II:

Phase I returns on Cycle Day 25. Phase I infertility returns on the evening of the fourth day of dry, nothing (Cycle Day 25) after the last day of the mucus patch (Cycle Day 21), or non-menstrual bleed.

This chart illustrates a non-menstrual bleed (Cycle Days 14–20), with two days of mucus as the bleeding ends. Mark Cycle Days 21 and 32 with a Δ because Cycle Day 21 is the last day of the mucus patch that follows a non-menstrual bleed and Cycle Day 32 is the last day of a mucus patch. Number the d,n days following the Δ accordingly (i.e., 1234). Apply the Mucus Patch Rule on the evening of Cycle Day 25.

Phase I Guidelines apply.

Phase III:

Not applicable since there is no thermal shift.

Note: On this chart there were 13 days of an unchanging pattern of mucus, but not 14 days which is a Basic Infertile Pattern. When a stretch of many days of a more-fertile mucus pattern like this does not end in ovulation, it is common to experience a non-menstrual bleed. Recall that the endometrium may build up so much that it cannot be sustained solely by estrogen. As a result, it breaks down and bleeding occurs.

Notes

BIP > Practice 1 (page 56)

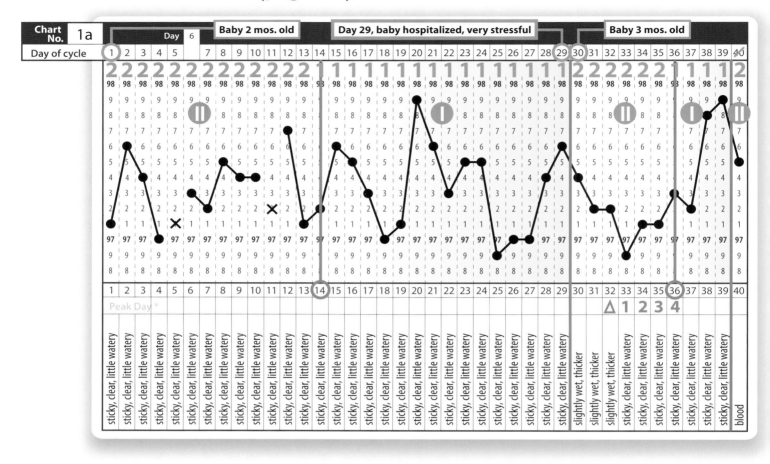

Phase I and II:

Phase I begins on the evening of Cycle Day 14 after a BIP is first established. Phase I returns on the evening of Cycle Day 36.

Since mucus descriptions remained the same during the first 14 days of this chart, a BIP was established and Phase I began on the evening of Cycle Day 14. Phase I continued until a change to the BIP was observed on Cycle Days 30–32, starting Phase II again. Days of BIP then returned. The last day of change from the BIP was marked with a Δ (Cycle Day 32) and the BIP days that followed were numbered accordingly (i.e., 1234). The BIP Rule was applied again, and Phase I returned on the evening of the fourth day of the return to the BIP (Cycle Day 36). Another change from the BIP occurred on Cycle Day 40, starting Phase II again.

Phase I Guidelines apply.

Phase III:

Not applicable since there is no thermal shift.

BIP > Practice 2 (page 58)

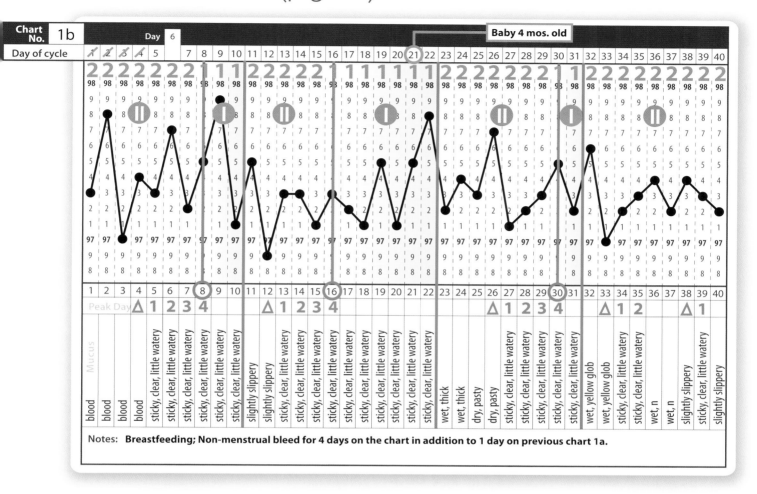

Chart No.	1b		Day	6																																			
Day of cycle	1̶	2̶	3̶	4̶	5		7	8	9	10	11	12	13	14	15	16	17	18	19	20	21	22	23	24	25	26	27	28	29	30	31	32	33	34	35	36	37	38	39	40

Notes: Breastfeeding; Non-menstrual bleed for 4 days on the chart in addition to 1 day on previous chart 1a.

Baby 4 mos. old

Phase I and II:

Phase I returns on the evening of Cycle Days 8, 16 and 30.

The chart is a continuation of the previous chart. Cycle Days 1–4 are considered fertile (Phase II) because of the non-menstrual bleed that carried over from the previous chart (Cycle Day 40 of BIP > Practice 1). The BIP returned after the bleed. The last day of the change from the BIP (a bleed) is marked with a ∆ (Cycle Day 4) and the BIP days that follow are numbered accordingly (i.e., 1234). Apply the BIP Rule, and Phase I infertility returns on the evening of the fourth day of return to the BIP (Cycle Day 8). Other changes from the BIP occurred on Cycle Days 11, 23, 32 and 36. The BIP returned, the BIP Rule was reapplied and Phase I infertility returned on the evening of the fourth day of return to the BIP on Cycle Days 16 and 30.

Phase I Guidelines apply.

Phase III:

Not applicable since there is no thermal shift.

The following practice charts are from women who have already established they are in early premenopause and therefore, can use the Mucus Patch and Basic Infertile Pattern Rules.

Mucus Patch Rule > Practice 1 (page 95)

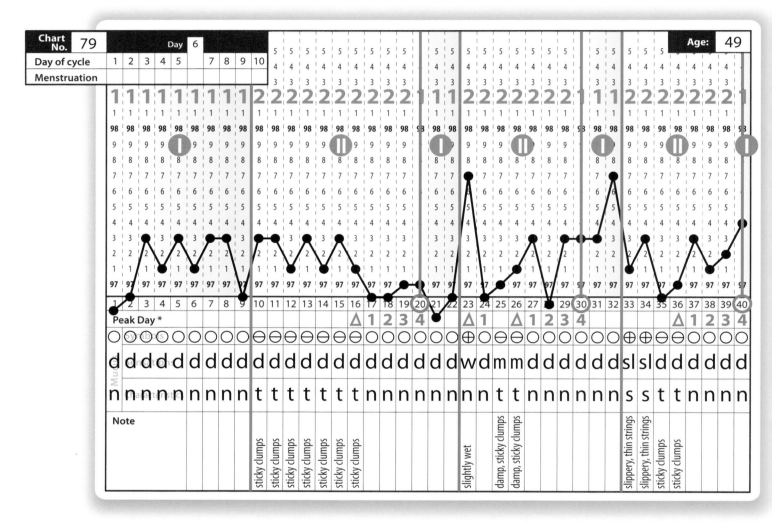

Phase I and II:

This woman was in Phase I at the end of her previous chart, so Cycle Days 1–9 are also Phase I. Mucus began on Cycle Day 10, and was on and off again several times throughout the cycle, thus the Mucus Patch Rule can be applied.

Phase I returns on Cycle Days 20, 30 and 40. Phase I infertility returns on the evening of the fourth day of dry, nothing (Cycle Days 20, 30 and 40), after the last day of the mucus patch (Cycle Days 16, 26, 36), or non-menstrual bleed.

Mark the last day of each mucus patch on Cycle Days 16, 23, 26 and 36 with a Δ.

Number all d,n days after accordingly (i.e., 1234). Apply the Mucus Patch Rule on the evenings of Cycle Days 20, 30 and 40.

Phase I Guidelines apply.

Phase III:

Not applicable since there is no thermal shift.

Notes

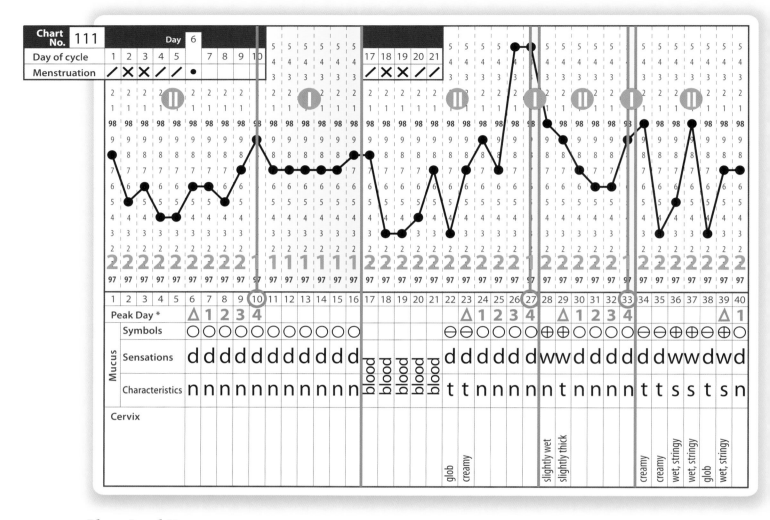

Phase I and II:

Phase I returns on Cycle Days 10, 27 and 33. Phase I infertility returns on the evening of the fourth dry, nothing day after the last day of mucus or non-menstrual bleed.

The bleeding episode from Cycle Days 1–6 is a non-menstrual bleed, so this chart starts in Phase II fertility. Another non-menstrual bleed occurred on Cycle Days 17–21, followed by two days of mucus and then dry, nothing days. Another mucus patch occurs on Cycle Days 28 and 29, followed by dry, nothing days, and then a final patch of mucus that lasts until Cycle Day 39. Mark the last day of each mucus patch or bleeding (Cycle Days 6, 23, 29 and 39) with a Δ. Number the d, n days after accordingly (i.e., 1234). Apply the Mucus Patch Rule on the evenings of Cycle Days 10, 27 and 33.

Phase I Guidelines apply.

Phase III:

Not applicable since there is no thermal shift.

BIP > Practice 1 (page 103)

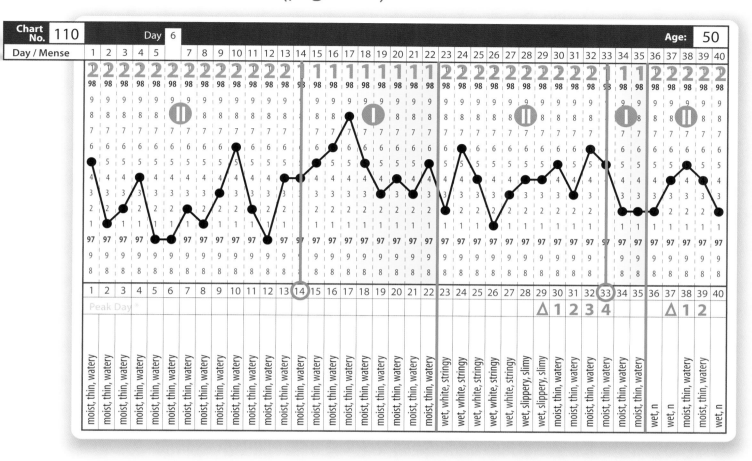

Phase I and II:

Phase I beings on the evening of Cycle Day 14 after a BIP is first established. Phase I returns on Cycle Day 33.

Since mucus descriptions remained the same during the first 14 days of this chart, a BIP was established and Phase I began on the evening of Cycle Day 14. Phase I continued until a change to the BIP was observed on Cycle Days 23–29, indicating a return to Phase II. Days of BIP then returned. The last day of change from the BIP was marked with a Δ (Cycle Days 29 and 37), and the BIP days that followed were numbered accordingly (i.e., 1234). The BIP Rule was applied again, and Phase I infertility returned on the evening of the fourth day of return to the BIP (Cycle Day 33).

Phase I Guidelines apply.

Phase III:

Not applicable since there is no thermal shift.

Chart No. 203					Day 6																															Age: 52			

Day / Mense: 1 2 3 4 5 — 7 8 9 10 11 12 13 14 15 16 17 18 19 20 21 22 23 24 25 26 27 28 29 30 31 32 33 34 35 36 37 38 39 40

Row of phase indicators: 2 2 2 2 2 2 2 2 2 2 2 2 2 1 | 1 1 1 1 1 1 1 1 1 1 | 2 2 2 2 2 2 2 2 2 2 2 2 2 1 | 1 1 1

Peak Day *

Circled days: 14 and 37

Mucus observations (Days 1–23): moist, n (each day)

Mucus observations (Days 24–40): wet, slippery, few strings (each day)

Phase I and II:

Phase I begins on the evening of Cycle Day 14 after the BIP is first established. Phase I returns on the evening of Cycle Day 37 after a new but different BIP is established.

The presence of mucus from Cycle Day 1 indicates Phase II. Since mucus descriptions remained the same during the first 14 days of this chart, a BIP was established and Phase I began on the evening of Cycle Day 14. Phase I continued through Cycle Day 23 until a change to the BIP was observed on Cycle Day 24, starting Phase II again. This mucus patch of wet, slippery, few strings established a new BIP after 14 days (Cycle Day 37), returning to Phase I infertility.

Phase I Guidelines apply.

Phase III:

Not applicable since there is no thermal shift.

BIP > Practice 3 (page 105)

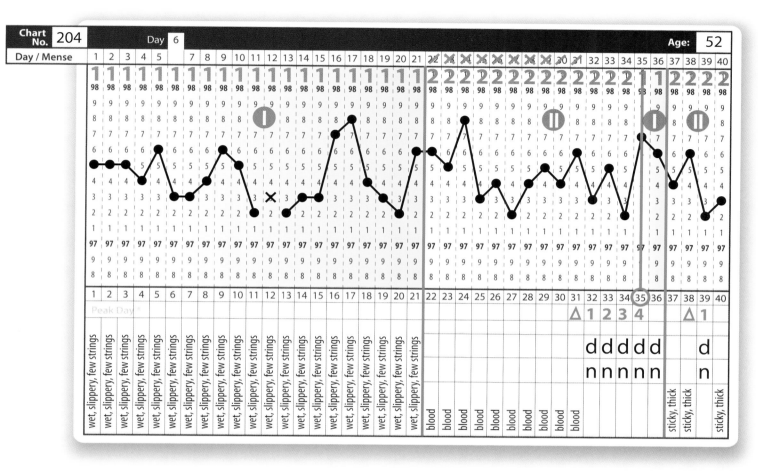

Phase I and II:

This chart is a continuation of the previous practice chart.

Phase I continues on Cycle Days 1–21 because a BIP was already established toward the end of the previous chart.

Phase I returned on Cycle Day 35. Phase I infertility returns on the evening of the fourth dry, nothing day after the last day of mucus or non-menstrual bleed.

Phase I continues through Cycle Day 21 because a BIP was established on the previous chart. A change from the BIP, a non-menstrual bleed, starts Phase II on Cycle Day 22. The non-menstrual bleed is followed by dry, nothing days, which means the Mucus Patch Rule can be applied. The last day of the non-menstrual bleed (Cycle Day 31) is marked with a Δ, and the d,n days that follow are numbered. The Mucus Patch Rule is applied and Phase I returns on the evening of Cycle Day 35.

Phase I Guidelines apply.

Note: A higher, yet constant level of estrogen can produce a BIP made up of more-fertile mucus. If progesterone is low, the endometrium may not be able to sustain itself and will slough off. Thus in these cases, a BIP of more-fertile mucus may be followed by non-menstrual bleeding.

Over the course of the previous chart and this one, the women had two different BIPs and then experienced mucus patches (Cycle Days 37–38 and 40) after a non-menstrual bleed.

Phase III:

Not applicable since there is no thermal shift.

Notes

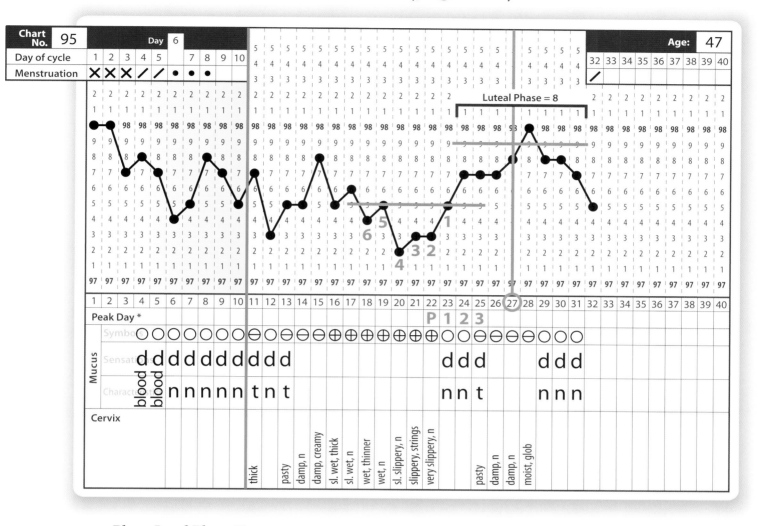

Phase I and Phase II:

- Day 5/6 Rule = Unknown (no cycle history provided)
- Doering Rule = Unknown (no cycle history provided)
- Last Dry Day Rule = 10
- Latest Day of Phase I = 10

Phase III

The third day of drying up past Peak Day is Cycle Day 25, and the three normal post-peak temperatures above the LTL are Cycle Days 24, 25 and 26. The third of these temperatures (Cycle Day 26) is below the HTL, and there is no cervix data. Thus, Phase III begins after waiting an additional post-peak day for another temperature above the LTL on the evening of Cycle Day 27.

Note that the length of the luteal phase is only 8 days (Cycle Days 24–31). Short luteal phases can occur during premenopause.

Long Luteal Phase > Practice (page 110)

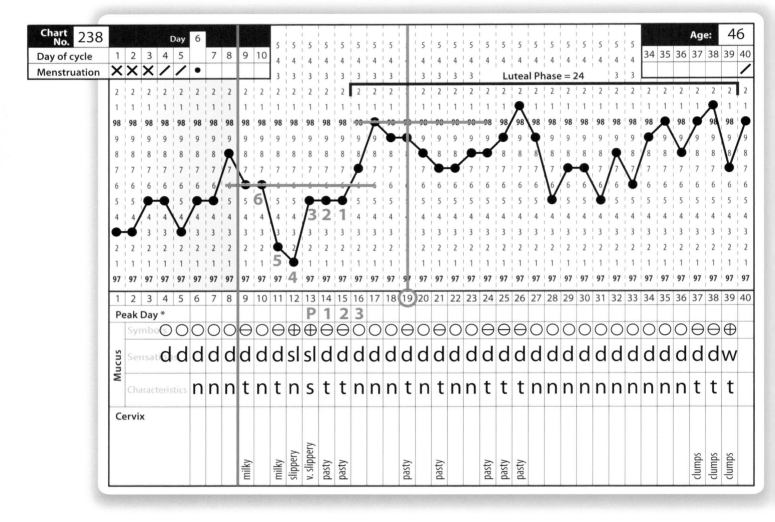

Phase I:

- Day 5/6 Rule = Unknown (no cycle history provided)
- Doering Rule = Unknown (no cycle history provided)
- Last Dry Day Rule = Cycle Day 8
- Latest Day of Phase I = Cycle Day 8

Phase III

The third day of drying up past Peak Day is Cycle Day 16, and the three normal post-peak temperatures above the LTL are Cycle Days 16, 17 and 18. The third of these temperatures (Cycle Day 18) is below the HTL and there is no cervix data. Thus, Phase III begins after waiting an additional post-peak day for another temperature above the LTL on the evening of Cycle Day 19.

While a 24-day luteal phase (Cycle Days 16–39) is uncommon in the absence of pregnancy, it may occur during premenopause.

Reference Guide R

Additional Resources

Breastfeeding

See *The Art of Breastfeeding* by Linda Kracht and Jackie Hilgert, The Couple to Couple League.

La Leche League International— www.llli.org

Natural Family Planning-supportive physicians

There are physicians who do not prescribe or recommend contraception, sterilization or abortion, nor will they refer to another physician for these services. Instead, these NFP-supportive physicians, also known as NFP-only physicians, use treatments that more directly address a woman's underlying condition, rather than possibly masking or potentially complicating these conditions by prescribing hormonal birth control. CCL teachers often know NFP-supportive physicians living nearby, so to find one a good place to start is to contact your teacher.

Another source of NFP-supportive physicians is the FertilityCare Centers of America. These centers have physicians trained in NaProTECHNOLOGY, which uses the biomarkers of the Creighton NFP model to recognize health and disease. You can search for a medical consultant at **www.fertilitycare.org**.

A third source to find an NFP-only physician in your area is One More Soul's website at **www.omsoul.org**. This organization maintains a database of NFP-only physicians, but note that some physicians listed are in specialties unrelated to women's reproductive health.

There are also physicians supportive of NFP but who also prescribe hormonal birth control. Often, such physicians can read an NFP chart and provide sound counsel to women. If you cannot find an NFP-only physician in your area, seek one who supports NFP. We have heard of many cases in which these physicians eventually discontinued prescribing or recommending birth control, sterilization or abortion after seeing patients who understand their fertility signs and apply NFP. Prayer and subtle encouragement are common actions that can lead to conversion.

Nutrition Information

Clinical nutritionists:
Contact the International & American Associations of Clinical Nutritionists to locate a clinical nutritionist near you: **www.iaacn.org** or 972-407-9089.

Nutrition as it relates to fertility:
See *Fertility, Cycles & Nutrition* by Marilyn Shannon (The Couple to Couple League, 2009).

Lochia

For about three to six weeks postpartum, women produce a blood-tinged discharge called lochia. Lochia occurs after childbirth because the uterus is contracting and shrinking back to its pre-pregnancy size and the endometrium is regenerating after the nine months of pregnancy.

For the first few days after childbirth, the lochia is composed mostly of blood; but it may also contain fragments of membranes from the amniotic sac and the coating and fine hair from the baby's skin. The color of this lochia is generally **dark red to brownish** and is called lochia rubra (meaning red).

Once blood flow decreases, the discharge becomes **thinner and brownish** in appearance and will contain plasma that oozes from the placental attachment site, white blood cells, and fragments of degenerating endometrium, all of which are part of the normal process of healing and regenerating the uterine lining so that a future baby could implant on the same site. This lochia is referred to as lochia serosa.[39]

---

[39] Francine Nichols, Ph.D. and Elaine Zwelling, Ph.D., *Maternal-Newborn Nursing – Theory and Practice* (W.B. Saunders Company, 1997), 980.

At approximately two weeks postpartum, the lochia becomes **thick and white to yellow-ish** in color and is called *lochia alba* (meaning white). It is composed of mucus (produced by all epithelial cell layers like the endometrium) and white blood cells which is what gives the lochia its white appearance. Lochia alba continues until three to six weeks postpartum, gradually decreasing in amount.

Note that this "mucus" is not related to fertility.

Postpartum

Return to Fertility > Formula-feeding

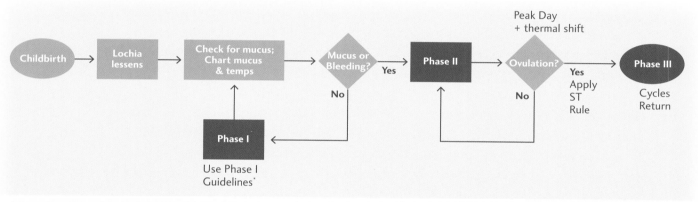

* Phase I Guidelines: Marital relations every other day; evenings only

Return to Fertility > Breastfeeding

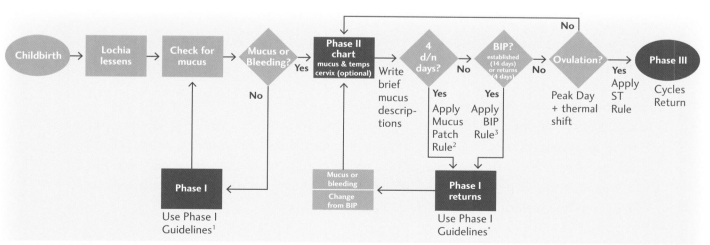

[1] Phase I Guidelines: Marital relations every other day; evenings only

[2] Mucus Patch Rule = Phase I infertility returns on the evening of the fourth dry, nothing day after the last day of a mucus patch or non-menstrual bleed.

[3] BIP Rule = Phase I infertility begins when a BIP is established, and returns on the evening of the fourth day of return to the BIP.

Strategies for recovery[40]

Cramping: The uterus continues to contract in the weeks after childbirth in order to return to its normal size. These contractions also help slow, and eventually stop, the postpartum bleeding by closing off tiny blood vessels in the uterine lining. Over the early postpartum weeks, these contractions may feel similar to menstrual cramps and may be more noticeable if you are breastfeeding, as the baby's suckling releases the hormone oxytocin. In addition to stimulating milk let-down, oxytocin contracts the uterus. If the discomfort (which can last up to six weeks) is more than mild or interferes with your breastfeeding, ask your doctor about pain relievers that are safe for you to take as a breastfeeding mother.

Constipation: Difficulty with bowel movements following birth is to be expected for several reasons, such as trauma to rectal (sphincter) muscles during delivery or increased levels of progesterone, which slow digestion and the passage of food through the intestines. This is a good time to focus on drinking plenty of water and obtaining a healthy amount of fiber through eating fruits, vegetables, and whole grains. If your doctor permits, mild exercise may also help.

Hemorrhoids: Many women find that if hemorrhoids did not develop during the later months of pregnancy, they resulted from the pushing and straining of the delivery. Focusing on nutrition (and especially fiber intake) is important here as well since you will want to try to avoid constipation. If your hemorrhoids are tender, warm sitz baths may help. Talk to your doctor if you have any concerns about their healing.

Vaginal pain: You can expect to have a sore and tender perineum for a time after giving birth due to the stretching and stress in this area. Some women are unable to avoid an episiotomy and will have stitches and a sore incision; others experience some minor tearing that needs to heal. Heat (warmth) promotes blood flow and promotes healing; therefore, warm (not hot) sitz baths are recommended. Cold decreases swelling and numbs the area, and thus ice packs can provide relief. Also, pay attention to personal cleanliness to help avoid infection. If healing is slow, or if you experience any sharp pains in your vagina, talk to your doctor.

Postpartum urinary incontinence: It is not unusual to experience temporary **urinary incontinence** (the inability to keep urine in the bladder) during the early weeks after childbirth. This is caused by the bladder muscles being stretched during late pregnancy and the delivery. As your organs and muscles return to their pre-pregnancy position, any incontinence should resolve itself. In the meantime, consider wearing a pantiliner if necessary, and talk to your doctor if this has not cleared up by your postpartum checkup.

---

[40] Information in this section was compiled primarily from William Sears, M.D. and Martha Sears, R.N., *The Baby Book* (New York: Little, Brown and Company, 2003), and William Sears, M.D. and Martha Sears, R.N., *The Pregnancy Book* (New York: Little, Brown and Company, 1997).

Hair loss: In the early weeks after childbirth, many women report that their hair seems to be falling out. In reality, the pregnancy hormones prevented the normal shedding of hair; and, as your hormone levels return to normal, hair loss may simply seem excessive. No treatment is necessary.

Exhaustion: This is one postpartum occurrence that is probably universal. As your body has likely been through the most strenuous work of your life, you can expect to feel a level of exhaustion that you may have never experienced before, as well as feeling achy and stiff for a while. There is no better strategy than to rest as much as possible and try to sleep whenever the baby sleeps. Rely on others for household assistance, and try not to worry about the work that may need to be done. Focus instead on your healing and on your baby.

Postpartum blues: Many mothers experience "weepiness" or sadness in the early days and weeks after giving birth. For 50–75% of mothers,[41] this is actually a normal experience that results from hormonal fluctuations. You may also experience mood swings, crying, anxiety, impatience, lack of concentration, etc. These symptoms are usually mild and disappear in a few weeks. Be sure to get plenty of rest, concentrate on your recovery, and rely on others for household help.

Postpartum depression: For 10–20% of mothers, the postpartum blues may develop into postpartum depression,[42] although postpartum depression (PPD) can also begin at any time during the first year. This can manifest itself as excessive fatigue, insomnia, changes in appetite, difficulty in making decisions, feeling hopeless, negative attitudes, and even thoughts of death or suicide. While PPD can be troubling, it is usually highly treatable, so be sure to talk to your doctor about what you are experiencing. (It is interesting to note that the higher levels of prolactin and oxytocin help decrease anxiety and are physiologically soothing to a breastfeeding mother.)

Nutritional Support during the postpartum transition

In order to minimize difficulties or promote healing from many of these postpartum occurrences, good nutrition is very important especially during the first six weeks postpartum. You should strive for a balanced diet of protein, complex carbohydrates (such as whole grains, fresh fruits and vegetables), and healthy fats. Avoid trans fats, processed vegetable oils which have been heated, and empty calories (such as sugary or pre-sweetened products). Be sure to include healthy essential fatty acids through certified toxin-free fish oils, cod liver oil, flaxseed oil, or healthy fish.[43] Many doctors recommend taking a vitamin/

---

[41] William Sears, M.D. and Martha Sears, R.N., *The Baby Book* (New York: Little, Brown and Company, 2003) 65.

[42] Sears and Sears, 66

[43] Toxin-free fish oils, including cod liver oil, are readily available at health food stores. For further information, see *Fertility, Cycles & Nutrition*, Fourth edition, and the National Resource Defense Council website: www.nrdc.org/health/effects/mercury.guide.asp.

mineral supplement that includes calcium. If you have not already done so, you may want to discuss this with your doctor.

Sexual satisfaction during the postpartum transition

New parents may also need additional insights into achieving satisfaction with their sexual relationships. One problem that can occur during a prolonged phase of infertility, especially with breastfeeding mothers, is an excessively dry vagina because mucus is not being produced due to the low level of estrogen. This normally can be overcome in a relaxed, unhurried environment where time is spent lovingly preparing the wife for genital intercourse. With slow and relaxing stimulation, the walls of the vagina release fluid due to vascular engorgement that occurs with sexual stimulation. This fluid acts as the primary source of vaginal lubrication for genital intercourse. A secondary but minor source of lubrication comes from the Bartholin's glands (special glands located slightly below and to the right and left of the vaginal opening), which release a few drops of lubricating fluid as well. To be emotionally and physically satisfying, sexual intercourse does not have to be tied to the estrogen production which occurs around ovulation. Rather, it is best tied to the loving touch and consideration between the husband and wife.

Nutritionally, vitamins A and E, zinc, and flax oil can help aid vaginal dryness. In addition, vaginal lubricants can be used during intercourse if necessary. If these nutritional and natural strategies do not alleviate the discomfort, see your physician.

Premenopause

End of Fertility > Premenopause

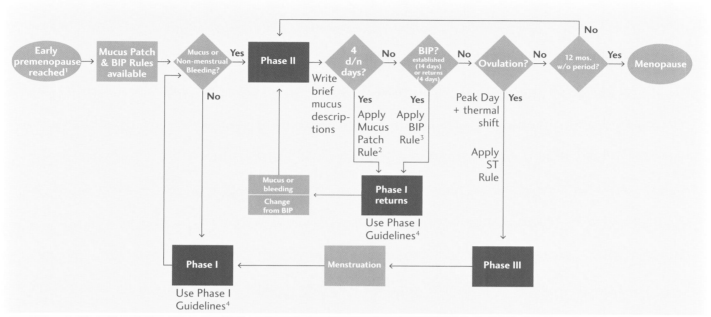

¹ Early premenopause begins when there is a persistent difference of 7 days or more in the length of consecutive cycles, where persistence is defined as recurrence within 10 cycles of the first variable length cycle.

² Mucus Patch Rule = Phase I infertility returns on the evening of the fourth dry, nothing day after the last day of a mucus patch or non-menstrual bleed.

³ BIP Rule = Phase I infertility begins when a BIP is established, and returns on the evening of the fourth day of return to the BIP.

⁴ Phase I Guidelines: Marital relations every other day; evenings only.

Possible Symptoms

While knowing how to read and interpret the key measurable signs of fertility during the premenopause transition is important, it is also good to be aware of several of the symptoms that may develop as a result of the changing hormone levels that are common at this time, such as:

- Irregular cycle lengths
- Spotting and/or bleeding
- Hot flashes and night sweats
- Vaginal dryness
- Mood swings, anxiety, depression
- Weight gain
- Sleep problems
- Problems with concentration and memory

Irregular cycle lengths: As you have already learned, cycle irregularities should be expected. This is normal as fertility declines. Generally, cycle length varies greatly and can be shorter or longer. Sympto-thermal observations and good chart recording will help. However, if you are not yet in your mid-forties, do not immediately assume that you are experiencing premenopause.

Read the chapter on premenopause in *Fertility, Cycles & Nutrition*, which will help you to see if there may be other possible causes for the cycle changes you are experiencing. An inadequate luteal phase is common in the forties and may explain mood swings due to premenstrual syndrome (PMS) which can occur at any age. (Remember that luteal phase inadequacy occurs because there is elevated estrogen and inadequate progesterone in the second half of a cycle. Good charting can help detect this problem because delayed ovulation followed by only a few days of elevated temperatures is typical of this hormone imbalance.) Since PMS can worsen during premenopause, try the suggestions in *Fertility, Cycles & Nutrition* on this topic. Better nutrition can be especially helpful at this age.

Another possible cause of cycle irregularities is **hypothyroidism** (low thyroid function), resulting from a lack of sufficient progesterone to stimulate the thyroid gland, or from other causes. Long menstrual cycles and very low temperatures (less than an average of 97.3° Fahrenheit taken orally before ovulation) on the NFP chart can be indications of low thyroid.

There are some conditions that may cause a woman to think she is in premenopause or menopause when, in fact, there may be other reasons for her cycle irregularities or lack of ovulations and periods. The most common examples are strenuous exercise and/or weight loss— being underweight or having insufficient body fat. If you are no longer having periods and are unsure whether or not this is due to menopause, you may want to consider having your FSH and LH tested by your doctor. These hormones remain elevated after menopause. (Conversely, an insufficient amount of body fat causes low FSH and LH and subsequent irregular or absent periods.)

Spotting and bleeding: Changes in menstrual flow are common at this time. Bleeding may appear unexpectedly as non-menstrual bleeding and could be fertile. If bleeding seems excessive, you should consult a physician. Heavy or prolonged bleeding may be the result of **uterine fibroids** (benign growths within the wall of the uterus), especially if you begin having heavy and/or painful periods during this time of life. If a medical checkup reveals that there are no fibroids or other serious medical conditions, try the suggestions in *Fertility, Cycles & Nutrition* under "Shorter, Lighter, and Pain-free Periods."

Hot flashes and night sweats: **Hot flashes** are sudden feelings of being extremely overheated, possibly to the point of breaking out in a sweat. When these occur during the night, they are commonly referred to as **night sweats**. They are caused by low estrogen, may last for only a couple of minutes, and occur rarely or several times a day. Some suggestions follow to help prevent or reduce the frequency and intensity of night sweats.

- Dress in layers so you can comfortably remove items of clothing during a hot flash.

- Avoid heavy blankets; use layers of lighter covers if necessary. Night sweats can disturb your sleep, so you want to minimize them as much as possible.

- Carry ice water, and avoid hot drinks that might provoke hot flashes.

- Keep a fan in your home and workplace to use as necessary.

- If you wish to avoid blushing during a hot flash, *Fertility, Cycles & Nutrition* suggests the following: "Exhale and hold your breath as the hot flash comes on. This initiates a reflex that causes the blood vessels in your skin to constrict, counteracting the blood vessel dilation of the hot flash."

- Try the nutritional strategies in *Fertility, Cycles & Nutrition*, especially flax oil and vitamin E.

If discomfort seems excessive, consult a physician.

Vaginal dryness and urinary problems: Another consequence of the decline in estrogen is vaginal dryness, a common symptom of premenopause and beyond that can cause vaginal irritation, make intercourse difficult and increase the risk of vaginal and urinary tract infections. Vitamins A and E, zinc, and flax oil can help. In addition, vaginal lubricants can be used during intercourse if necessary. If these nutritional and natural strategies do not alleviate the discomfort, see your physician.

Mood swings, anxiety, and depression:[44] **Mood swings** are short-term changes between moods and anxiety, irritability or feeling "the blues." You can often improve mood swings, anxiety, and depression by stabilizing blood glucose levels and nourishing the adrenal glands.

- Eat meals and snacks that include protein, complex carbohydrates, and healthy fats, such as yogurt, whole wheat bread, seed-nut-raisin mixes (using almonds, macadamia nuts, Brazil nuts, filberts, hazelnuts, peanuts, pine nuts, pecans, pistachios, pumpkin seeds, sesame seeds, sunflower seeds, walnuts), granola cereal, rice germ, wheat germ, cheese and crackers, peanut butter, avocados, olives, beef, and dairy.

---

[44] Information in this section was compiled primarily from Shannon, Fourth edition; *Eat Right to Live Long* by Dr. Cass Ingram, N.D. (Hiawatha, Iowa: Cedar Graphics, 1989) 142; and *Depression-Free, Naturally* by Joan Mathews Larson, Ph.D. (The Random House Publishing Group, 1999) 82.

- Avoid foods containing trans fats, such as margarine, processed cheeses, deep-fried foods, shortening, peanut butter with hydrogenated fat, potato chips, and bakery goods. Also avoid processed meats such as hot dogs, sausages, pork rinds, and bologna.

- Reduce or avoid sugar, artificial sweeteners, and caffeine. Too much sugar causes a rapid rise in blood glucose levels with a subsequent reactive drop that causes the adrenal glands to secrete stress hormones that produce nervousness and anxiety. In the short term, caffeine stimulates the adrenals, but in the long term, it causes the adrenals to become more exhausted due to overstimulation.

- There are a variety of nutrients that are also necessary for healthy functioning of the adrenal glands. Properly nourishing these glands can produce "calmer nerves, improved sexual desire, and normal estrogen in the body."[45]

Weight: Modest weight gain during premenopause is natural and healthy because the body is adjusting to hormonal changes. However, maintaining weight without becoming obese requires adequate exercise and carefully selecting the right foods to eat. Being underweight and having low body fat can cause cycle irregularities, including a lack of ovulation and periods. In addition, thin women are more prone to hip fractures in part because they have "less padding," to protect the hip if they fall.

Sleep problems: Avoid work or exercise immediately before bedtime. In addition, avoid large meals, alcohol, sugar, and caffeine. Use of computers, tablets, or devices with bright screens immediately before bed can make it more difficult to fall asleep.

Problems with concentration and memory: Eat foods that will help to maintain steady blood glucose levels, such as protein, complex carbohydrates, and healthy fats (as discussed earlier under "Mood swings, anxiety, and depression"). The B vitamins are very important for cognitive function, especially B6, folic acid, and B12. It is very important to get enough sleep to improve cognitive function and to decrease stress — specifically, eight hours of sleep in a dark room. If necessary, take naps in order to meet your body's requirements.

Risk of osteoporosis: Osteoporosis is a condition in which the bone mass is reduced and the bones are more fragile.[46] Both men and women naturally lose bone mass from about their mid-thirties. In women, this loss is accelerated by the decrease in estrogen that comes with menopause. Throughout our lives our bones are constantly being broken down and rebuilt; after menopause the rate of breakdown is faster than the rate of rebuilding and some women are at increased risk of fractures. These occur primarily in the spine, wrist, and hip.

---

[45] Shannon, Fourth edition.

[46] National Osteoporosis Foundation, *www.nof.org*.

Sufficient calcium is critical; women over 50 need 1200 mg per day (taken with vitamin D to allow absorption) from diet and supplements. In addition, regular weight-bearing exercise is a must! Bone is living tissue — old bone is dissolved by **osteoclasts** (bone "eating" cells and new bone is created by **osteoblasts** (bone-building cells). Osteoblasts respond to pressure — walking, jogging, running, jumping, lifting — by adding new bone where it's needed for maximal strength so weight-bearing exercise is necessary to "pressure" your bone cells into keeping your bones strong. (In contrast, astronauts in weightless space endure rapid and substantial bone loss because there is no pressure exerted on the osteoblasts to re-build strong bones.)

Perhaps the most practical way to prevent fractures is by developing good safety habits — making behavioral changes now that will decrease the chance for fractures. Implement safety measures to prevent falls, such as using hand railings on steps, keeping small items and pets from being underfoot, and walking (not running) up and down steps. It is also important to conscientiously maintain good posture in order to avoid deformities of the spine.

Thyroid

Healthy functioning of the thyroid gland is critical for adequate hormone levels. During both the postpartum and premenopause transitions, it is not unusual to have cycle changes that are actually tied to a poorly functioning thyroid gland rather than the result of the normal hormonal fluctuations of the time. For a discussion of the importance of a healthy thyroid gland on the fertility cycle, nutritional suggestions for low thyroid function, and medical testing for thyroid deficiency, see Chapter 7 of *Fertility, Cycles & Nutrition* by Marilyn M. Shannon.

Vaginal dryness

Vaginal dryness can occur during the postpartum transition as well as during the premenopause transition. Once menopause is reached, vaginal dryness is even more common. The primary cause for vaginal dryness is low estrogen. A woman's body is designed to produce enough estrogen during those times when she is not cycling (i.e.,postpartum, premenopause, menopause) to prevent sexual intercourse from being irritating or painful, and to maintain the integrity of the vaginal tissues. But, there are times when this does not occur; nutritional strategies may help alleviate this condition. Vitamins A and E are especially helpful. See *Vaginal Dryness* on page 157.

G Glossary

Abstinence: The practice of refraining from indulging an appetite or desire, i.e., sexual intercourse.

Amenorrhea: Absence of menstrual periods.

Androgens: Male hormones produced by the adrenal glands that become more prominent in women as estrogen declines. These hormones normally will increase a woman's sexual desire.

Antibodies: Proteins that fight infections.

Asthma: A disease of the respiratory system.

Bartholin's glands: Special glands located slightly below and to the right and left of the vaginal opening that release a few drops of lubricating fluid during marital relations. The main source of vaginal lubrication, however, comes from release of fluid from the vaginal walls through sexual stimulation.

Basal body temperature: The temperature of the human body at rest or upon awakening, unaffected by food, drink, or activity.

Basic Infertile Pattern (BIP): An infertile, unchanging mucus pattern that lasts for at least 14 days This phenomenon sometimes occurs during the postpartum or premenopausal transitions.

Basic Infertile Pattern (BIP) Rule: A rule used to determine the beginning of or return to Phase I infertility during the postpartum or premenopause transitions. Phase I infertility begins when a BIP is established and returns on the evening of the fourth day of return to the BIP.

Bellagio Consensus Conference on lactational infertility: A conference held in Bellagio, Italy in 1988, in which family planning experts from around the world met and discussed research on the return of fertility. Specifically, they looked at mothers who were exclusively breastfeeding a baby, and not using any method of family planning or fertility awareness. As a result, this group issued a Consensus Statement with regard to exclusive breastfeeding and its correlation to amenorrhea.

Breastfeeding: See continued breastfeeding, exclusive breastfeeding, and mixed breastfeeding.

Cervical mucus: A natural fluid of the body that is necessary for the proper functioning of a woman's reproductive system and is an aid to fertility.

Cervical os: The opening of the cervix.

Cervix: The lower, narrow part of the uterus that extends slightly into the vagina; the opening to the uterus.

Change of life: A woman's transition from her fertile, reproductive years through the declining fertility of premenopause, to the post-reproductive status of menopause.

Changing mucus pattern: A pattern of mucus in which the mucus sensations and/or characteristics change frequently, but do not disappear.

Colostrum: Yellowish liquid secreted by a mother's breasts for about the first three to five days following childbirth. Colostrum is rich in antibodies and contains more protein and minerals, and less sugar and fat, than breast milk produced later.

Continued breastfeeding: Nursing beyond six months, when the introduction of other foods and liquids are added to complement the breast milk. The baby still nurses and pacifies at the breast on his own schedule.

Continuous mucus: A mucus pattern that is sometimes experienced by women who are postpartum or premenopausal; not to be confused with vaginal discharge. (See changing, and unchanging mucus patterns.)

Corpus luteum: A yellow, progesterone-secreting structure that forms from an ovarian follicle after the release of a mature egg. If the egg is not fertilized, the corpus luteum secretes progesterone for approximately 14 days after ovulation.

Day 5/6 Rule: A rule to determine the infertile time at the beginning of a woman's menstrual cycle. In the absence of mucus, infertility is assumed on Cycle Days 1-5. For women with cycles of 26 days or longer in the last 12 cycles, infertility is assumed on Cycle Days 1-6.

Diabetes mellitus: A metabolic disorder affecting blood sugar levels; can cause kidney, eye, and nerve damage.

Doering Rule: A formula to determine the infertile time at the beginning of a cycle based on the earliest day of temperature rise in previous cycles. In the absence of mucus, the last day of Phase I infertility is seven days before the earliest first day of temperature rise.

Endometrium: The inner lining of the uterus.

Estrogen: A fertility hormone that causes the cervix to undergo physical changes and to secrete mucus, and which causes the development of the endometrium.

Exclusive breastfeeding: Nursing whenever the baby indicates a desire (day or night) during his first six months of life; the baby receives no bottles or early solids, stays near his mother and pacifies at the breast on his own schedule.

Extended Phase I infertility: Those days, weeks, or months during which a woman experiences dry, nothing days or a Basic Infertile Pattern; can occur during the postpartum or premenopause transitions.

Fertile time: The time of a woman's menstrual cycle leading up to and including the time of ovulation, characterized, in part, by the presence of mucus. Sexual intercourse during this time (Phase II) could result in conception.

Fertility: The quality or condition of being able to produce offspring.

Fertility monitor: A device that measures hormone levels, such as estrogen or Luteinizing Hormone (LH), to detect the fertile time of a woman's cycle.

Follicle: One of thousands of small ovarian sacs containing an immature ovum; each cycle, one follicle fully matures and is released at ovulation. Upon release of its egg, the follicle becomes a structure called the corpus luteum.

Follicle Stimulating Hormone (FSH): A fertility hormone secreted by the pituitary gland to stimulate the maturation of ovarian follicles.

Formula feeding: A baby is fed with a bottle and receives only milk, ranging from donor milk, to specialty formulas, to cow's milk.

Hemorrhoids: Painful varicose veins in the canal of the anus.

High Temperature Level (HTL): The temperature level that is 0.4° Fahrenheit (0.2° Celsius) above the Low Temperature Level (LTL); used to establish the beginning of Phase III with the Sympto-Thermal Rule.

Hodgkin's disease: A malignant form of lymphoma marked by progressive enlargement of the lymph nodes and spleen and sometimes of the liver.

Hormone: A chemical substance produced by a gland or organ of the body and carried by circulation to other areas where it produces an effect.

Hot flash: A sudden feeling of being extremely overheated, possibly to the point of breaking out in a sweat; caused by low estrogen levels, typically occurring during premenopause and menopause.

Humanae Vitae (On Human Life): Pope Paul VI's 1968 encyclical letter explaining the duty of the transmission of life for married couples.

Hypercholesterolemia: An unusually high level of cholesterol in the blood.

Hypothyroidism: A state of low thyroid function, resulting from a lack of sufficient progesterone to stimulate the thyroid gland, or from other causes.

Induced lactation: The process by which a non-pregnant mother is stimulated to lactate.

Infertile time: The time of a woman's menstrual cycle both before the ovulation process begins as well as after ovulation, characterized, in part, by the absence of mucus. Sexual intercourse during these times (Phases I and III) does not result in conception.

Lactate: To produce milk; lactation continues when breastfeeding.

Lactational amenorrhea: Lack of menstrual periods due to breastfeeding.

Lactational Amenorrhea Method (LAM): A method of family planning based on the high infertility during the first six months postpartum for mothers in amenorrhea who exclusively breastfeed.

Last Dry Day Rule: A formula to determine the infertile time at the beginning of a cycle based on the appearance of mucus. The end of Phase I is the last day without mucus sensations or characteristics.

Less-fertile mucus: Often described as tacky, sticky, opaque, or thicker in characteristics than more-fertile mucus. Less-fertile mucus sensations are usually described as moist, damp, or sticky. This type of mucus is usually present both before a woman experiences more-fertile mucus leading up to ovulation and after Peak Day, as part of the drying up process; could also occur during Phase III.

Leukemia: An often fatal cancer of the blood forming organs leading to an abnormal increase in white blood cells.

Lochia: The blood-tinged discharge a woman experiences for about three to six weeks after childbirth.

Low Temperature Level (LTL): The highest of the normal pre-shift six temperatures. The LTL is the level from which the High Temperature Level (HTL) is determined.

Luteal phase: A stage of the menstrual cycle, lasting about two weeks, from ovulation to the beginning of the next menstrual flow; measured by counting the days from the first day of temperature rise to the last day of the cycle.

Luteinized unruptured follicle: A follicle that starts to become luteinized and begins to act like a corpus luteum by producing progesterone, but without releasing an egg. Can occur in a premenopausal woman, and may be indicated by a longer than normal luteal phase without pregnancy.

Luteinizing Hormone (LH): A fertility hormone produced by the pituitary gland that helps to stimulate ovulation in females.

Lymphoma: A tumor in the lymph node.

Menopause: The permanent cessation of menstruation that is officially reached after 12 months of no menstrual periods. Menopause typically occurs around age 51, but may occur earlier or later than this age.

Menstruation: The periodic discharge of blood and tissue from the uterus in non-pregnant women following a sustained thermal shift; occurs from puberty to menopause.

Mixed breastfeeding: Formula or pumped breast milk given in addition to breastfeeding prior to giving solid food.

Mood swings: Short-term changes between moods and anxiety, irritability, or feeling "the blues."

More-fertile mucus: Mucus that is present during the fertile time prior to and including ovulation (Phase II) in a woman's menstrual cycle. It is identified by sensations of wetness and/or slipperiness, and/or characteristics that are stretchy, stringy, or resembling raw egg-white. More-fertile mucus may sometimes be present at other times when estrogen levels are higher without ovulation, such as during a Basic Infertile Pattern, more commonly found during the postpartum or premenopause transitions.

Mucus characteristics: The qualities of mucus that a woman sees and/or touches when making observations.

Mucus patch (patches of mucus): One or more days of mucus sensations/characteristics.

Mucus Patch Rule: A rule used to determine the return to Phase I infertility during the postpartum or premenopause transitions. Phase I infertility returns on the evening of the fourth day of dry, nothing after the last day of the mucus patch or non-menstrual bleed.

Mucus sensations: The qualities of mucus that a woman feels and senses throughout the day and when wiping at bathroom visits.

Mucus symbols: The graphic symbol used to describe the day's mucus observations: ◯ = no mucus, ⊖ = less-fertile, ⊕ = more-fertile.

Natural Family Planning (NFP): A means of reading a woman's signs of fertility and infertility; also known as fertility awareness.

Night sweats: A sudden feeling of being extremely overheated, possibly to the point of breaking out in a sweat, that occurs during the night; typically caused by low estrogen.

Non-menstrual bleeding: A bleeding episode that is not preceded by a thermal shift, and therefore, is not related to a prior ovulation. It can appear as spotting or days of bleeding. Non-menstrual bleeding can mask the presence of mucus, and thus can be a potentially fertile time.

Osteoblasts: Bone-building cells.

Osteoclasts: Bone-dissolving cells.

Osteoporosis: A condition in which the bone mass is reduced and the bones are more fragile.

Ovary: The female reproductive organ containing the ova, or eggs.

Ovulation: The process of an ovarian follicle releasing its ovum, thus making a woman able to become pregnant.

Oxytocin: A hormone released from the pituitary gland that stimulates the contraction of the smooth muscles of the uterus during labor, facilitates release of milk during nursing, and assists in postpartum bonding; commonly referred to as the "hormone of love."

Peak Day: The last day of the more-fertile mucus before the drying-up process begins. Peak Day can only be identified in retrospect.

Perimenopause: A term commonly used by the medical profession to refer to the years that encompass the change from normal ovulatory cycles to the cessation of menses.

Phase I: A time of infertility, beginning when a woman starts her menstrual bleeding and ending when fertility signs appear.

Phase II: The fertile time of the cycle. It is during this time that the woman ovulates and when conception may occur.

Phase III: The infertile time after ovulation.

Pituitary gland: A gland located at the base of the brain that releases various hormones that control the functions of other organs.

Placenta: The organ inside the uterus that supplies food and oxygen to, and removes waste from, the unborn baby through the umbilical cord.

Postpartum: The term used to explain that a mother has recently given birth and has not yet returned to her pre-pregnancy state.

Postpartum blues: Weepiness or sadness in the early days and weeks after giving birth, resulting from hormonal fluctuations.

Postpartum depression (PPD): Excessive fatigue, insomnia, changes in appetite, difficulty in making decisions, feeling helpless, negative attitudes, and thoughts of death or suicide; usually highly treatable.

Postpartum urinary incontinence: Temporary incontinence (inability to control bladder) during the early weeks after childbirth.

Premenopause: The natural life progression that occurs as a woman's fertile years gradually come to a close; the years leading up to menopause. It can begin as early as age 35, although the average age at the start of premenopause is 43; often referred to by the medical community as perimenopause.

Pre-shift six: Six lower temperatures immediately preceding at least three temperatures that rise above them in a sustained pattern; used to set the Low Temperature Level (LTL).

Progesterone: A fertility hormone secreted by the corpus luteum that prepares the uterus for the fertilized ovum and helps sustain a pregnancy.

Prolactin: A hormone that aids in the accelerated growth of breast tissue during pregnancy. With suckling, prolactin increases and the hormone stimulates and maintains the secretion of milk, and enables natural bonding between mother and baby. Commonly referred to as the "the mothering hormone."

Responsible parenthood: The virtuous decisions made by a married couple to plan or to postpone conception through the knowledge and practice of fertility awareness.

Seminal residue: Seminal fluid that remains in a woman's vaginal area after she has sexual intercourse.

Short luteal phase: A luteal phase less than 10 days; can result from the corpus luteum producing insufficient progesterone.

Suckle: To feed from the breast.

Sympto-Thermal Method (STM): A method of fertility awareness that utilizes the observation of changes in the cervical mucus, basal body temperature, and cervix to determine the fertile and infertile times of a woman's menstrual cycle.

Sympto-Thermal Rule: A formula to determine the infertile time of a woman's menstrual cycle following ovulation. Phase III begins on the evening of: 1) the third day of drying-up after Peak Day, combined with 2) Three normal post-peak temperatures above the LTL, and 3) The third temperature at or above the HTL or the cervix closed and hard for three days. If these conditions are not met, then Phase III begins after waiting an additional post-peak day for another temperature above the LTL.

Thermal shift: At least three temperatures that are higher than the six preceding temperatures; used to calculate the Sympto-Thermal Rule and Temperature-Only Rule.

Unchanging mucus pattern: A mucus pattern experienced by some women who are breast-feeding or are premenopausal in which the mucus sensations, characteristics and quantity remain the same each day; could appear right after the lochia ends or later, sometimes for a period of time.

Urinary incontinence: The inability to keep urine in the bladder.

Uterine fibroids: Benign growths within the walls of the uterus which may result in heavy or prolonged bleeding.

Uterus: A hollow, pear-shaped organ in which a baby grows during the nine months of pregnancy; frequently called the womb.

Vagina: The female genital canal extending from the uterus to the vulva.

Vaginal discharge: A discharge that could be the result of an infection sometimes characterized by an odor and/or is unusual in appearance, and could be irritating or painful.

Weak temperature rise or delayed thermal shift: A shallow or weak thermal shift consisting of temperatures that do not rise far above the LTL, that drop to or below the LTL, or that occur quite a bit later after Peak Day.

Index

K

Kegel exercise, 122
Kennedy, K., 24
Kracht, Linda, 29, 149

L

Labbok, M., 25
Labia, 8, 33, 46
Lactate, 27, 162
Lactational amenorrhea, 20, 22–25, 162; factors that influence, 23
Lactational Amenorrhea Method (LAM), 25, 162
La Leche League International, 26, 149
Larson, PhD, Joan Mathews, 157
Last Dry Day Rule, 14, 63, 162
Lauwers, J., 29
Leukemia, 27, 162
Lochia, 31–33, 40–41, 150–151, 162
Low Temperature Level (LTL), 162
Luteal phase, 61, 107, 111, 156, 162; long, 109, Practice Chart, 110, 148; short, 107, 117, 120, Practice Chart, 108, 147
Luteinized unruptured follicle, 109, 162
Luteinizing hormone (LH), 7–8, 19, 79–81, 156, 162
Lymphoma, 27, 162

M

Marital intimacy, 70–73, 121–122
Marital relations, 13, 32, 34, 42, 62, 89, 119
McNeilly, A., 24
Memory, 155, 158
Menopause, 77, 82, 162
Menstruation, 20, 162; menstrual cycle, 6; non-menstrual bleeding, 42, 96–97
Miscarriage, 120
Mixed breastfeeding, 22, 24
Mood swings, 155–157, 162
Mucus, 32–33, 41–61, 88–106; absence of, 8, 42, 90, 116; after bleeding, 49–53, 96–98; Basic Infertile Pattern (BIP), 53–58, 99–105; brief descriptions, 43–44, 91–92; cervical, 160; changing pattern, 59–60, 105–106, 161; characteristics, 8–9, 162; continuous, 53–61, 99–106, 161; in premenopause, 88–106; internal, 46; less-fertile, 162; more-fertile, 162; patches, 45–53, 93–98; patterns, 43, 53, 90, 95; presence of, 8; recording of characteristics, 9; recording of sensations, 8; sensations, 8, 163; shininess,

44, 92; symbols, 9, 163; typical pattern, 12; unchanging pattern, 53–58, 99–106, 164; while breastfeeding, 41–61; with bleeding, 49–53, 96–98
Mucus patch, 45–53, 93–98, 162
Mucus Patch Rule, 45–46, 49, 51, 55, 93–95, 97, 101, 106, 111, 114, 162; Postpartum Practice Chart 1, 47, 132; Chart 2, 50, 134; Chart 3, 52, 136; Premenopause Practice Chart 1, 56, 140; Chart 2, 58, 142

N

NaProTECHNOLOGY, 149
National Osteoporosis Foundation, 158
National Resource Defense Council, 154
Natural Family Planning (NFP), vii, 163
NFP consulting, 16
Nichols, Ph.D., Francine, 150
Night sweats, 78, 155–157, 163
Non-menstrual bleeding, 32, 42, 49–53, 80, 96–98, 156, 163

O

Obesity, 27
O'Connor, K.A., 80
One More Soul, 150
Osteoblasts, 159, 163
Osteoclasts, 159, 163
Osteoporosis, 28, 158, 163
Ovarian cancers, 28
Ovary, 6, 20, 163
Overweight, 27, 158
Ovulation, 6, 8, 12, 20, 24, 39, 43, 90, 106–107, 163; first postpartum, 39; immature egg, 120
Oxytocin, 20, 28, 163

P

Pacifier, 24
Peak Day, 9, 12, 163
Perez, A., 25
Perimenopause, 82, 163
Peterson, Anne, 25
Phase I, 6, 11, 39, 55, 101, 163; extended infertility, 161; guidelines, 13, 32, 42, 88, 96; marital relations in, 13, 32, 34, 42, 89; rules, 13–14
Phase II, 6, 11, 32, 39, 42, 49, 87, 89, 96–97, 163
Phase III, 6, 39, 87, 163; rules, 14